BLACK HOLES
AND TEPEE RINGS
On Cosmic Mysteries & Spiritual Mythology

Robert M. Watkins

BWP

Black Wolf Productions

Kalispell, Montana

Robert M. Watkins is a retired consulting petro-
leum engineer residing near Kalispell, Montana.
He is the author of an earlier book, *The Ugly Face
of Power: And Masks of Deception.*

Black Wolf Productions
P.O. Box 565
Kalispell, Montana 59903

Copyright© 1994 by Robert M. Watkins

Library of Congress Cataloging-in Publication Data
Watkins, Robert M.
Black Holes & Tepee Rings: on cosmic
mysteries and spiritual mythology
Includes appendix with notes and bibliography, index
1. Natural science, 2. Human consciousness,
3. Philosophy/Mythology

CIP #93-090417

Book design by author
Cover design by Brian Sackett
Cover art by Daniel J. Krause
Typesetting and graphics by Ray Wright of Grizzly Graphics

ISBN
0-9637006-2-6

Manufactured in the United States of America

Dedication

To all those who contributed to my understanding of this mysterious and wonderful world in which we find ourselves.

Acknowledgments

This book was a long time in the making, beginning with what I learned from my parents and early teachers, ending with the last book I read. Many of my best teachers were professional colleagues and associates, clients, and friends who shared their knowledge and expertise covering a broad spectrum of disciplines. My wife Nancy gets credit for opening my consciousness to new ways of knowing and understanding. To all those who nurtured my curiosity, I now express thanks.

Special recognition goes posthumously to Black Elk of the Oglala Sioux Nation and physician Richard M. Bucke; and gratitude to The University of Nebraska Press for keeping Black Elk's philosophy in print, and the same to E.P. Dutton and Company concerning Bucke's work.

Specific credit and thanks for permission to include excerpts goes to Joseph Epes Brown from his book *The Spiritual Legacy of the American Indian*, 1982, The Crossroad Publishing Co.; Stephen W. Hawking and the Permissions Department of Bantam Books for use of material from *A Brief History of Time: From the Big Bang to Black Holes*, 1988, Bantam Books; Gary A. Kowalski and Stillpoint Publishing for use of material from *The Souls of Animals*, 1991; the Institute of Noetic Science to quote David B. Chamberlain, from *The Outer Limits of Memory*, the Autumn, 1990, Noetic Science Review; Dr. Brian O'Leary, Ph.D., from his book *Exploring Inner and Outer Space: A Scientist's Perspective on Personal and Planetary Transformation*, 1989, North Atlantic Books; and Rupert Sheldrake, from his book, *The Presence of the Past: Morphic Resonance and the Habits of Nature*, 1988, Vintage Books.

Also, recognition goes to Brian Sackett for the cover layout and design; and Ray Wright for his editorial assistance, typesetting, and graphics. Finally many thanks to my friend and former business partner, Daniel J. Krause, for the cover painting.

Contents

Black Holes & Tepee Rings

FOREWORD

Curiosity is a mental demon which torments the mind of man. Like a resident ghost, it has haunted my mind since earliest memory. Even while quite young my parents grew weary of an endless series of questions, most of which had the preamble: *how* or *why*. They provided a few answers, but mostly I heard phrases like "I don't know" and "never mind about that." I also got into trouble several times because of taking something apart to see how it worked, particularly so when I couldn't put it back together.

I wanted to know a little about everything. Since nobody seemed willing or able to answer my questions, it reduced to a matter of finding the answers myself. Though it might appear something of a paradox, considering my curiosity, I wasn't a particularly good student in school. They just didn't teach the things I wanted to know. At least that's the way it seemed at the time. School days dragged by, I could hardly wait for the bell so I could go down by the river or up on the mountain to mingle with the creatures of nature (we lived in a rural area and I attended a small country school). The out-of-doors was my classroom of choice because there I found the answer to some of my questions. Then after starting high school I discovered the library. I took a lot of those books home, not textbooks which would produce good grades, but those containing subjects a level or two beyond my curriculum.

Reading was and remains more than a hobby or pastime; it became a primary way of knowing. My interest covered a broad spectrum of subjects: religions and mythology because of the mystic visions they convey, science has also become mystic for laymen and scientists alike during the past few decades (when referring to science, it includes the various branches of physics, geology, biology, medicine, psychology, philosophy to some extent, and the mysteries of the paranormal); history because it traces the evolution of thought, consciousness, and human behavior.

Despite my lack of attention in school, curiosity led me into engineering. I wanted to know how things worked; physics, chemistry, and mechanics revealed many answers about the physical world. But the "other world" remained a mystery.

In bygone times this other world was the domain of religion and mythology, and from this realm came hundreds of ideas and beliefs. Nowadays, not to be outdone by sages and prophets, scientists intrude into the mystical. This new science casts a shadow over many of our old concepts of reality. It hasn't resolved many of the older mysteries, it has merely enlarged their scope, even introducing more unknowns.

This book isn't intended for scientists, nor as comprehensive scientific discourse. Instead, it purports to reveal a few of the many mysteries underlying physical existence. It's written for curious people, who like me, can't refrain from asking *how* and *why*. The book is merely an introduction to the mystic dimensions of nature; I invite the reader to embark upon a personal journey through the cosmos in search of answers. (The Appendix lists a few helpful references, identifies the source of quotes, and offers some brief explanations about more technical topics).

I try to maintain the implied covenant between science and engineering. That is, science directs itself toward investigation, observation, and conclusions leading to the formulation of theories which define the laws of nature. Engineering converts those theories and laws into practical application. Science would be little more than an academic pursuit without engineering; engineers couldn't exist without the findings of science. The two disciplines are interwoven, co-dependent. I take many liberties with science throughout the book, much more so than a scientist would dare. Though I have tried to accurately present the many quotes contained herein, the conclusions are strictly mine and do not necessarily represent the thinking or opinion of those quoted. Any errors, improper interpretations, or faulty reasoning are mine. I readily admit that the myth is exactly that—a myth. But it works, at least for me.

Let me define myth as used throughout the book. Modern societies tend to pervert the true meaning of the word. A myth is usually considered a falsehood, a lie, a fabrication designed to conceal the truth. Used in the proper context, a myth *is* a fabrication, but not intended to deceive or hide the truth. A myth illuminates vague ideas, it sheds light on that which is otherwise unexplainable. Bishop and Darton[1] provide a good working definition of myth. They say, "A myth...tries to find a way of conveying a truth too profound to be dealt with in matter-of-fact terms." Therefore, in a practical sense religions are mythology because they explain an obscure concept which can't be understood any other way.

The term metaphysics carries many connotations but my use of the word conforms with the first definition contained in Webster: *after those things relating to external nature, after physics.* I interpret external things to be those we can dissect, measure, weigh, and in general observe directly. Metaphysical things include the mysteries, the unknowns, beauty and wonder and order. It would also include Spirit. I therefore view nature as having two complementary components: the physical universe in which we presently reside, and Spirit, the animating force which gives it life.

One last definition: I use the term Creator throughout the book as a way of including all the various concepts of a deity central to different spiritual traditions. You may think of the Creator as God, Allah, the Great Spirit, or however you perceive a deity. I refer to the Creator as He/She, not necessarily to appease feminists, but because the myth merges the masculine with the feminine to form Unity, or the One.

I'd like to give a definition of Spirit and spiritual but I don't know how. Since I make liberal use of these terms, I need to convey some idea as to what I mean. First, I'll say what they don't mean: spirit is not a capricious entity who visits evil pranks on mankind, spirit is not a discarnate entity who haunts old houses, spirit is different from one's soul, spirit is not physical. I envision Spirit as a radiant essence emanating directly from the Creator. It would be an ethereal energy field containing infinite love, compassion, and knowledge; it constitutes the substance of life itself. If not one and the same, Spirit is second only to the essence of the Creator as the most profound mystery of all.

I don't propose that you accept my myth at face value. I haven't found the answer to all my questions, and probably never will. And some of my answers are merely metaphors and analogies, abstract ideas which allow me to make sense of that which remains forever unknowable. I acknowledge the limited scope of the myth. Many gaps exist, particularly about the paranormal, personal psychic abilities, the strange world of dreams, to name a few. I accept these phenomena, but they were not crucial in formulation of the myth. A path is what I seek, a union with Nature, becoming as one with all that is.

It is not my intent to deride or discredit existing religions and mythologies. Instead, the myth acknowledges the aura of mystery which surrounds Nature and the Creator, it is a summons to personal spiritual mythology—a blending of new ideas with old traditions. It is a supplement to, not a replacement of, a pre-existing belief system. My hope is that the book may stimulate your thinking so you too may be inspired to create a personal myth—a way of life which includes spiritual imperatives and a reverence for Nature.

Chapter One

THREE COSMIC MYSTERIES

The more we learn, the more mysterious our world becomes. The simple days of yesteryear are gone. With each passing year comes a flood of new ideas, strange findings, knowledge which threatens our long-held concept of reality. We can either deny this new knowledge, or we can try to make sense of it.

Back in yesteryear, when I was a lad, the world was stable, predictable, clearly defined. Nearly all of us common folk (those following the Western tradition) believed the world to be about 6,000 years old. It had come into being by the handiwork of an omnipotent Creator; at some point in the not too distant future it would come to an end. At Armageddon the faithful would ascend to heaven, those left behind...well, you know the story. Nothing mysterious here, it was very straightforward, told in down-to-earth terms.

This simple and easy to grasp idea of the world and the cosmos became increasingly inadequate as new information filtered through to a better educated public. I suspect that for the majority of us World War II was quite a turning point. We began hearing about strange things such as radar, sonic submarine detection devices, guided missiles, an ever-expanding assortment of high-tech devices. Beyond doubt, August of 1945 was a pivotal point in our understanding of the physical world.

I began my Junior year in high school a month after the detonation of the first atomic bomb. I'd been looking forward to the physics class because splitting the atom was a concern of everybody on Earth. Much to my disappointment, our teacher didn't know any more about atomic fission than did a fifth grade grammar teacher (all information was classified). So we studied Ohm's law and Newtonian physics, bare basics. During college years we began hearing rumors about the strange happenings at sub-atomic levels—no details, just enough information to shake our confidence in physical reality. Unknown to us at the time, physicists were working on a different atomic process involving the fusion of hydrogen atoms. From this work emerged the dread hydrogen bomb and an escalating arms race between the United States and the Soviet Union. We then faced a mystery which threatened to annihilate mankind.

Mysteries induce fear in some people, curiosity in others. I fit into the latter group. But it was quite some time before comprehensible information became available to the average lay person. All such knowledge originally circulated within the scientific community. However, by the late 1960s a few scientists began to speak more openly, even writing articles that one could understand (a put-up job by The Atomic Energy Commission to gain acceptance of nuclear power generation, I suspect). Beginning in the 1970s, entire books written for the lay person became available. It soon became apparent that our classic impression of physical reality may be little more than an illusion.

A Changing World View

Man's curiosity concerning reality reaches back into antiquity. In times past, reality reduced to speculations involving the origin and destiny of man, coupled with assumptions concerning the role of a supernatural being, or beings. These mysteries fell within the purview of shamans and mystics, then later with the priesthood. Each era and each culture wrestled with the problem and each created a myth to explain, or comprehend, the unknown.

Western Society adopted Hebrew mythology and Aristotle's philosophy without asking many questions. Though the average lay person never questioned this view of reality, a wave of restless curiosity began rippling the water of conventional thinking nearly 500 years ago. Rebels such as Copernicus and Galileo concluded that Earth was not the center of the universe as Aristotle had proclaimed. Intellectual prowess continued to gain momentum in northern Europe as small groups of curious individuals probed the mysteries of nature. By the turn of the eighteenth century European investigators had difficulty reconciling their observations with established orthodoxy. Natural science, being yet an infant and heretical in the view of the clergy, received its nourishment from behind closed doors by tight lipped naturalists. Then Frenchman René Descartes opened a new door for Western thought by restoring philosophy to classical traditions. Next, Isaac Newton stepped forth with the first comprehensive work in physics. Meanwhile others were studying Earth and speculating about its history. With publication of *The Origin of Species* in 1859, Charles Darwin snipped the last thread binding science to theology. Albert Einstein ushered in the twentieth century with two new theories of relativity which shattered all previous concepts of reality. Others founded the study of quantum mechanics which was even more mystical than relativity. We laymen didn't hear much about these new developments; indeed, not many scientists understood the implications.

As the twentieth century unfolded, science essentially commandeered the study of origins. Physics, relativity, and a new understanding of matter enabled astrophysicists to construct theories concerning the beginning of the Universe. Geologists pieced together an incredible account of Earth's history. Biologists traced the origin of life back some three to four billion years. Anthropologists stayed busy unraveling the origin of mankind. Since little, if any, of the new information fits exactly with the mythologies of old, we must adopt a new view of nature, and a supplemental myth to go along with it.

The current scientific view is primarily deterministic because physical systems are observable and often conform to mathematical description. Physicists can construct models of an expanding universe, geologists can explain how mountains rise and sediments become deposited, physicians can tell us how blood circulates in the body and what causes babies. We have a fair understanding of physical systems; our knowledge of metaphysical systems is grossly inadequate. For instance, how and why did life originate, what is the nature of consciousness, where are memories stored, what causes the wide swing in human emotions and behavior? Mathematics can't give an answer to such mysteries. Therefore, we need to create a modern myth, a way of understanding which integrates the physical with the metaphysical.

It was indeed a happy event for free thinking

persons when science and medicine broke free from the restrictions imposed by theology. Had it not been for the scientific revolution, we would probably still be traveling in a horse and buggy, burning wood for heat, and most of us wouldn't live beyond the age of fifty years. But we've paid a price for progress: this new freedom of scientific thought increasingly minimizes the role of a Creator in the affairs of the Universe. That is, the more we discover about the physical Universe, the less significance we attach to the divine purpose in the order of things. In retrospect, we could argue that theology, being largely the fabrication of a self-serving priesthood, in itself has little to do with divinity—hence nothing was lost.

But the diminished authority of theology left a vacancy in the heart and mind of Western Society. By turning to science to explain reality, we no longer recognize, or acknowledge, the mystery and wonder of nature. This spiritual void prompts us to become an overly materialistic culture. We put today's pleasures and comfort ahead of fading spiritual imperatives. We can trace many of our social and economic problems, either directly or indirectly, back to our emphasis on leisure, entertainment, and the accumulation of possessions. It's an unhappy situation because spiritual bankruptcy is the price paid for rampant materialism. We're left without a spiritual myth to live by.

But let's not cast stones at science. It has given us many tools and a wealth of information without dictating how to use either (politicians usurped this prerogative). Science concerns itself with the study of physical systems. It deals with the concrete through observation and experiment; the application of scientific principles permits us to build automobiles, computers, and vehicles that take us to the moon. None of our technical devices are malevolent in themselves, it's how we use them which causes wars and crime and other social abuses.

We have come to know a lot about nature's physical systems. Unfortunately, we are still in the dark ages concerning nature's metaphysical systems. Nature is more than glowing galaxies, devastating earthquakes, and subatomic particles. Nature is also about life. And life is more than mere biology and physiology: it includes spiritual properties such as emotion, intelligence, consciousness, will, intent and purpose. These topics have to do with metaphysical systems. My personal hypothesis is that we will never have a complete understanding of nature until we integrate the physical with the metaphysical, the tangible with the intangible, the temporal with the eternal. In short, science is yet limited in what it can tell us about reality: too many mysteries remain. But science tries, as follows:

Mystery Number One—The Initial Condition[1]

One could reasonably think that some initial state existed before the Universe came into being. But what were the properties of the Initial Condition? Has the Universe always existed, thereby eliminating the necessity for an Initial Condition? Or did all universal matter lay stored in some gigantic cosmic warehouse awaiting use by the Creator? Or, was the initial state an energy form, which after undergoing some specific process, energy became universal matter. Or, did the Creator start with nothing and end up with a universe? The last question may sound flippant but it happens to be the answer that modern physicis finds most acceptable.

According to scientific mythology, and in keeping

with a time honored but slightly altered preamble, we can begin this myth as follows: "Once upon a time, before time, everything that is, lay crunched within a tiny bubble of nothing." Like an earlier myth, it was without form, and void, and in darkness.

In mathematical jargon that tiny speck of nothing is known as singularity. This means that everything that now exists erupted from a container smaller than the period after this sentence. Time was yet waiting to happen. Space and matter did not exist. There was nothing but a lonesome Creator. Who, other than a Creator or mathematician, can conceive all that space and matter coming forth from a tiny dot?

Singularity is a mathematical phenomenon, an abstract concept which doesn't begin to describe a physical condition. From a lay viewpoint, we know nothing more about the initial state than that contained in Genesis. Thus we encounter the first great mystery.

Mystery Number Two—A First Cause

Why? How?

Why did the Creator desire a universe, and how did it spring forth from nothing?

Though a few physicists may ask of themselves *why* the Universe came into being, none can begin to give us an answer, they don't even try. This is strictly a metaphysical question, the traditional territory of theologians and philosophers. Their answers are many and varied, and despite the vehemence with which they defend their respective ideas, the true answer remains unknown. We can and will speculate concerning the *why*, but in the end we must acknowledge that the intent of the Creator remains a profound mystery.

Science isn't reluctant to offer theories concerning

how the First Cause came; indeed, considerable investigation and debate surrounds the first event. A tacit assumption exists which states that if time were run backward to the First Cause, the Initial Condition would reveal itself. Then, by knowing the initial state, all the mysteries of the Universe would collapse into a compact law of nature. In short, we would know the Mind of the Creator.

If you thought singularity a difficult concept, get ready for another superlative: The Big Bang theory postulates that the initial singularity exploded into a gigantic fireball containing sub-atomic scraps of matter and scorching radiation. It expanded with unimaginable speed. Temperatures soared beyond comprehension. Simultaneous with the Big Bang, the hands on the cosmic clock began turning, an inferno roared inside a rapidly expanding sphere of space. A millionth of a second after ignition, protons began precipitating from the cosmic plasma, ten-thousandths of a second later electrons came into existence. Within one second the average temperature had dropped to ten billion degrees centigrade, ten times that in the interior of our Sun. Frenzied high energy particles collided, annihilating one another, and showering space with huge amounts of hot radiation. As the rapid expansion progressed, the temperature decreased to about a billion degrees allowing electrons and protons to join forming hydrogen and helium atoms.

Thus, according to Big Bang theory, the First Cause was not a gentle and passive event. It does lack the burden of six long and arduous days of labor (however, it will soon become apparent that Creation is still in progress).

Gravity came into being early in the first second following the Big Bang. It caused an attraction between primal material which later caused huge clouds of hydrogen and helium to form. Gravity continued its work by bringing clumps of matter within these clouds into closer association. The more dense the cloud of hydrogen and helium became, the stronger the force of gravity.

By some process not fully understood, galactic size clouds of gas began to collapse, or compress. Smaller pockets of gas precipiated within these clouds to later become the primal material for individual stars. Gravity continued to exercise its authority, producing very dense neophyte stars. Since compression increases the temperature of any gas, fledgling stars eventually became so hot at the core that fusion of the individual atoms began. A star then becomes a thermonuclear reactor radiating huge amounts of energy (light). Typically, a galactic cloud contains enough mass to produce 100 to 200 billion stars. Our Sun therefore is only one of many in the Milky Way Galaxy, and our galaxy is only one of several hundred billion other galaxies scattered throughout the Universe. It's hard to think that Mother Earth was central to the Creator's intent— why expend such wasteful effort when we could get along just fine with nothing more than our solar system?

The Big Bang theory of Creation is certainly more spectacular than anything envisioned by the ancients, but it also has credibility problems. Singularity poses a conceptual problem for laymen. Of concern to physicists, calculations based on the theory fail to predict the Initial Condition prevailing just before the Big Bang. The theory allows a quantitative description of cosmic evolution back to what's called Planck time,* that being an instant just 10^{-43} second after ignition of the fire-

---

*So named in honor of Max Planck (1858-1947), German theoretical physicist generally regarded as the man who founded quantum theory.

ball. That's a pretty small increment of time—to write it out longhand, one would place a decimal point followed by 42 zeros and the numeral 1 (0.000 . . . . . 1). We laymen would consider this minute gap of ignorance inconsequential. But not so for physicists because at Planck time all the known laws of physics break down. Hence, failure to establish the First Cause hides the Initial Condition, which in turn conceals the intent of the Creator. Big Bang theory tells us nothing about the first two mysteries; the Mind of the Creator is yet unknown.

Most physicists accept Big Bang theory believing that they still have more to learn concerning basic physics. A few, however, envisioned a different process. Three prominent European physicists (Sir Fred Hoyle, Thomas Gold, and Hermann Bondi, all three then associated with Cambridge University) proposed a rival theory which flourished back in the 1950s and early 1960s. Termed the Steady State model, they suggested that matter is being continuously created within inter-stellar space to replace that which expands out beyond the visible universe. This theory gained honorable respect for a time, but as additional data concerning the Universe became available, technical problems arose which caused the theory to lose credence.[2]

One problem which discredited the Steady State model was an inability to hypothesize a process allow-ing the instantaneous appearance of matter from noth-ing. Atoms of hydrogen and helium from nothing and coming from nowhere? Is this more mysterious than a universe emerging from singularity? This objection to the Steady State Universe is reminiscent of the Biblical passage, "gagging at gnats and swallowing camels." However, our lay viewpoint has grounds for criticism because the Steady State model also fails to define the

Initial Condition and a First Cause event. The intent of the Creator remains a mystery. Regardless of all objections, the Steady State model implies an ambitious Creator, one still toiling away in the manufacture of matter. We could admire this Creator for dedicated service and diligent pursuit of His/Her goals, whatever they may be.

Mystery Number Three—The Ultimate Destiny Of The Universe

Science has thus far rendered little understanding concerning the first two mysteries. This shortcoming does not discourage physicists from indulging in speculation concerning the future; that is, making predictions concerning the ultimate terminal event, the fate of the Universe. We will excuse this indulgence because the final event may shed light upon the Creator's plan—give us a peek into the Mind of He/She who established the Initial Condition and instigated the First Cause.

Since the Universe contains all of nature, both the physical and spiritual components, its fortune may also foretell the fate of Spirit, and by implication, that of the Creator. Nonchalantly accepting the Big Bang model, let's consider three alternate fates, all predicated upon the Big Bang model.

A Closed Universe?

The *closed* model, starting with a big bang, would expand at a decreasing rate, finally stop, and then collapse due to the force of gravity. Expansion (the present mode) would be an evolutionary process leading to improved conditions favoring the advancement of life. The contraction phase would be chaotic, a process devoid of conditions essential to life. All life forms would eventually go into extinction sometime late in the expansion, probably beginning with the highest forms and sliding down the scale to microbes. The Big Crunch would be a return to the Initial Condition, after which another big bang might occur. We can think of this model as oscillating universes—a continuous succession of big bangs and big crunches. A closed Universe implies an eternal Creator having unlimited power who exists both before and after physical time.

An Open Universe?

An *open* universe would result if the inertia of the expansion exceeded the gravitational attraction between galaxies and other matter (mass). That is, gravity would be insufficient to cause a slow-down and eventual collapse. Our Universe would expand forever. As stars burned out and galaxies moved farther apart, the average temperature would drop. Eventually it would approach absolute zero.[3] At absolute zero all chemical reactions cease, all atomic activity comes to a standstill. The Universe is dead. This final state is sometimes called the *heat death*, presumably because the Universe will lack ordered or usable heat. In scientific terms, this state represents a condition of maximum entropy[4] (total chaos).

With an open universe, advancing biological systems would dominate during its mid-life, then stabilize at some unknown point, and eventually deteriorate. Increasing chaos (entropy) would lead to massive extinctions among all life forms which may then exist throughout the cosmos. This model suggests a Creator who, needing a break or diversion, created the Universe in a moment of whimsy or for amusement. After the heat death, the Creator could then return His/Her attention to more important affairs. This idea is distasteful because it removes any hint of cosmic purpose, it leaves us as robots wandering in random orbits.

A third possible model is known as a *flat* universe. This idea postulates an expanding universe which *almost* runs out of steam at a late stage. It doesn't have enough kinetic energy to keep up with an open universe, it doesn't have quite enough mass to cause gravitational collapse. It, like the open model, would continue to expand forever except at a slower rate. There is little difference between its destiny and that of the open model—they both die a heat death.

The flat model didn't originate at a cocktail party as one might suspect. At first glance we see little difference in the ultimate fate of either the open or flat models. Why bother with such a theory at all?

It came about because the calculated rate of expansion just slightly exceeds the rate which would result in a closed system. Since a visual inventory reveals less than 10% of the matter necessary to close the Universe, it's logical to think that invisible matter lurks somewhere in the universal shadows. Perhaps the estimate of the velocity of expansion is excessive, or in the alternative, initial estimates of the hidden mass are insufficient. Whichever, the flat model is not conclusively definitive; it suggests the need for further investigation. Moreover, the flat model poses another metaphysical dilemma. If the Creator was shooting for a closed Universe to match other natural systems which we can observe today, the flat model suggests a near-miss. It represents a slight miscalculation, a little mistake while establishing the Initial Condition. Failure to create enough mass in the beginning is indicative of a careless Creator. Sloppy workmanship on the part of the Creator! This we find hard to accept because other natural systems seem to run with perfect precision.

Since the Steady State model has fallen from favor, and we don't care to indict the Creator for negligence as in the flat model, we find ourselves left with either an open or closed model.

Perhaps it's more than just coincidence that the flat model is borderline. With a little more mass here and there, the Universe would close. With a little less, the Universe would continue expanding forever. How do you resolve the question?

The Quest for the Missing Mass

You conduct a search for the missing mass, if any.

A few cosmologists around the world pursue a diligent search for as yet undiscovered universal material. Toward this end, they seclude themselves in observatories, they labor with long mathematical equations, and when they lay down to sleep the question lingering in their mind is, "where is the missing mass?"

Several theories exist which could conceivably furnish enough additional matter to cause gravitational collapse resulting in a Big Crunch. One idea is that small phantom particles called neutrinos could account for the missing mass. Not much is known about neutrinos except they came into being during the early turbulence of the infant Universe. They are elusive, hard to detect, and their physical properties basically unknown. They seem to scamper through the Universe oblivious to the known forces of physics, unimpeded by barriers, totally nonchalant as they go about whatever business they do. It's not even certain that they constitute mass. So, the neutrino idea is nebulous to say the least.

A more recent idea, called superstring theory, postulates that strands of *dark matter*[5] permeate the Universe. Dark means that it is invisible to current detection apparatus, so finding and conducting a physical inventory of this material is presently impossible. Perhaps enterprising physicists will develop a method to detect and quantify the physical properties of neutrinos, or, they may discover a new means of finding and identifying dark matter. The history of science contains abundant examples of having found ways to circumvent the impossible. Thus, we probably haven't heard the last of these theories.

A search for the missing mass will no doubt continue unless another idea comes along. Superstrings, the neutrino idea, indeed the Big Bang model itself, are all merely theories.

We should remain mindful that a theory isn't law, it's more like an idea entered in a beauty contest. If a theory has simple elegance, and cannot be disproved with existing knowledge, it's likely to gain popular support. But supporters are fickle because when another beauty comes along a new winner takes the throne. A theory, like a beauty contestant, can undergo cosmetic surgery to remove blemishes and unsightly disabilities. Theories evolve, either becoming simpler, more complex, or abandoned all together.

The Big Bang theory is still in a state of uncertainty because it cannot determine the Initial Condition nor offer a suggestion concerning a First Cause. And without additional data (the missing mass), neither can it precisely define the final condition. Another problem associated with any theory of the Universe is that what we see today actually happened millions and billions of years ago. This is because it can take that long for the light from distant galaxies to reach us. Peering through a telescope is exactly the same as looking backward in time. What we see "way out yonder" happened billions of years ago when the Universe was much smaller.

The Big Bang theory does explain much of what cosmologists see happening in the Universe. Observational evidence clearly indicates that distant galaxies are receding from one another, some at velocities approaching the speed of light. The Big Bang model provides the mechanism to propel all that mass, but it fails to identify the source of energy. We can't be positively certain that Big Bang theory is correct, it just happens to be the most accepted idea in circulation today.

The origin and fate of the Universe are not an immediate concern. Life for all of us will go on just the same whether or not the missing mass exists. But for many of us, the quest for the missing mass (judging the fate of the Universe) has profound philosophical and metaphysical implications. It gives us a glimpse into the Mind of the Creator.

How so? If the Universe is destined for death, it would seem that the Creator is either temporal, or not much concerned about us and our cosmic home. If temporal, He/She would not be omnipotent as the many spiritual traditions insist. Life and the Creator would perish when the last star flickered out. The last shred of consciousness would fade away with nothing or nobody left to retain even a memory of what was. To think of a Creator as being either indifferent or temporary removes any hint of divinity, or purpose behind the grand order which we perceive around us.

On the other hand, an oscillating universe would suggest eternal consciousness and an omnipotent Creator. Though all *physical* things would perish in the terminal phase of one universal lifetime, spiritual consciousness (the Mind of the Creator) would continue uninterrupted. After returning to the Initial Condition, a new universe could come into being. Universes and worlds unending would be more in keeping with spiritual imperatives.

Maybe cosmologists will eventually penetrate the present barrier imposed by Planck time thus enabling them to define the First Cause, which in turn may reveal the Initial Condition. With these two mysteries resolved, the terminal event may become apparent. Until then, however, any explanation concerning the three cosmic mysteries reverts to metaphysics.

Another possibility exists, but for now we will assume that the Universe sprang forth from a singularity and that the missing mass will be found. We will consider the alternative later, but in all cases the Creator will have spiritual imortality.

*Bit by bit, piece by piece,
year after year, are all
things made.*

Chapter Two

STARDUST TO SYMPHONY

The Mystery of Emerging Life

How could a fireball of unimaginable chaos eventually result in billions of galaxies, stars, planets, and moons?

What process transformed the energy contained within the cosmic egg into immortal symphonies, classic literature, celebrated works of art?

Back in yesteryear almost any Sunday School student could have answered these questions. But not so today. The best minds in the world can only give us a sketchy idea as to how galaxies and stars came into being. Not a single biologist can tell us how physical matter became living creatures. The appearance of life on Mother Earth remains another profound mystery.

Perhaps you might consider the above questions impertinent: what difference does it make? If so, be reminded that how we view ourselves and regard our place in nature influences our behavior, and our collective conduct may affect the fate of our species as well as other life forms. Also, man is a curious creature ever striving to discover his origins, always questioning the meaning of things, perplexed concerning his purpose here on planet Earth. And finally, the more we learn, the better we can serve that purpose—whatever it is.

The Building Blocks of Nature

Recall from Chapter One that the infant Universe following the Big Bang was a turbulent ball of boiling hydrogen and helium atoms. Hot radiation and a host of neutrinos accompanied this mass of particles. Then when the early chaos subsided and temperatures dropped to tolerable levels, the Universe settled down to engage in some serious evolution.

Hydrogen, then as now, was the most abundant element in the Universe. Helium was second. These two elements are the primal components of all physical matter. So, this leads to several questions. For instance, from whence came the oxygen to combine with hydrogen to form water which is essential to every living thing on Earth, or the carbon to build muscles and fiber? From whence came the calcium for teeth and bones, the iron which circulates in our bloodstream, the other 14 trace elements needed by our body? Where did the silicon needed for sandy beaches and granite mountains originate? And who needs helium? Other than filling balloons for children's birthday parties, it is inert and serves no direct role in support of biological systems.

Obviously, the Big Bang didn't finish the work of Creation. It only started a long sequence of events, a process which began with primal material and transformed it into beings capable of writing and conducting a symphony.

Recall from the last chapter that galactic sized clouds, called nebula, fragmented into smaller globules, each of which contracted as gravity exerted its influence. These fragments of primal gas continued to impode until eventually they became very hot in the interior. The lights of the galaxy began to flicker when the other three forces of nature became active.[1] Thermonuclear reactions ignited hydrogen fusion in the core of first generation stars. These first born stars emitted huge amounts of radiation, visible light being one product. Thus, our galactic home came into being.

Unlike men, all stars are not created equal. Some are smaller than our Sun, others much larger. It's the big fellows to whom we owe our existence. They gave their life to manufacture the heavier elements from which mountains and men arise.[*]

Like men, stars pursue a natural life cycle—birth, life, and eventual death. Small stars have a long life because they consume their inherent energy much slower than more massive stars. When their supply of hydrogen burns out they simply cool off to bcome a cosmic remnant. Mediocre stars like our Sun have a shorter life because the increased gravitational force elevates core temperatures, causing more rapid fuel consumption.

At the core of Father Sun is a giant thermonuclear reactor which operates like the dread hydrogen bomb (nuclear fusion). However, unlike the bomb which explodes with devastating effects, the overburden weight of outer gasses confines the reaction within the core. The core is extremely hot and under high pressure. This causes four hydrogen atoms to fuse together forming one atom of helium. The fusion of hydrogen releases enormous amounts of energy. The energy resulting from millions of fusions each second propagates to the Sun's surface. From there, energy radiates in all directions throughout the Universe at the speed of light.[**]

[*]Used in this sense, man or men refers to humans, species Homo *sapien sapien*.
[**]Light travels 186,000 miles per second, equivalent to going around Earth's equator seven times a second.

A very tiny fraction of this energy reaches the surface of Mother Earth.

Visible light, or its absence when our face turns away from the Sun, denotes day from night. Infrared light melts the snow on my lawn, it evaporates water from Earth's oceans and redistributes it in the form of rain over arid land regions, it maintains the temperature on Earth within the narrow tolerance required by biological systems. Ultraviolet light, if not deflected by a layer of ozone high in the atmosphere, causes skin cancers on naked creatures like man. These energies (the three varieties of light), when combined in the proper proportion, drive a process called photosynthesis. From this process comes plant life and the oxygen needed by all respiratory creatures. The source of all our energy comes directly or indirectly from a nuclear reactor located some 93 million miles from Earth. Without the Sun's energy all life on Earth would perish in a very short time.

Our Sun is now about half-way through its expected 10 billion year life. Near the end of its life it will expand dramatically, its size ballooning out to about Earth's present orbit. Mercury, Venus, and Earth will in turns become whists of vapor. At this stage the Sun will become a red giant desperately attempting to retain its solar identity. But alas, due to its intermediate size, the nuclear furnace will be unable to burn the helium manufactured during earlier phases. Our Sun will slowly cool and shrink to become a dense white dwarf about the size of planet Earth. As it cools the outer plants will die from heat deprivation. Our solar system will shrivel to a clump of cold cinders and a lifeless cloud of vapor and dust. Parades, slogans, protests, and sit-ins will not circumvent this final ecological disaster.

But a star, say three times larger than our Sun, has an even shorter life cycle. Its larger mass not only speeds up fuel consumption, it gives gravity license to exercise increased authority. Core temperatures soar much higher, causing increased thermonuclear activity. Helium atoms fuse forming carbon, the fusion of carbon creates oxygen, oxygen fusion forms silicon, silicon fuses into iron. Then the process ceases. The dying star sheds its lightweight outer layers, the remaining heavy elements implode toward the core. The strength of gravity forces electrons into the nucleus of atoms where they combine with protons to form nothing but neutrons which are extremely dense. Such a stellar corpse is now a neutron star having a diameter of about 20 miles; a teaspoon of this material would weigh about 40 *billion* tons (a condition about as difficult to conceive as singularity).

If stellar evolution ended here all the building blocks of life would lay locked up in the cooling core of burned out neutron stars. The Universe itself would eventually become largely inert: a few small stars still flickering, the corpse of larger stars emitting a faint glow of radiant heat.

But this doesn't always happen. The reason: very large stars from 10 to 50 times as big as our Sun keep the Universe alive. If not for them we could not exist.

These giants are a minority; their life is much shorter than our Sun. Life for a big star begins the same as for smaller stars, the same thermonuclear reactions occur as in a neutron star, but their final demise is much more spectacular. They die a violent death. Gravity causes a sudden collapse of in-falling material toward a previously formed neutron core. It then rebounds from the core, causing a gigantic explosion. Within seconds a supernova releases more energy than the star had during its entire life. The radiance may be brighter than the entire galaxy in which it resides. The rare elements of nature, including those vital to life forms, synthesizes within the fireball. A huge cloud of rapidly expanding gas and dust particles (newly formed elements) mushrooms into interstellar space. This nebula glows brightly for a few months then cools due to expansion and dissipating radiation; the remaining core becomes just another spinning neutron star.[2]

The nebula formed by a supernova contains all the building materials required to manufacture a congregation of smaller stars. More important from our perspective, its dust also contains the material to form planets and solar systems. Every atom in our body (about 10^{28} on average) except hydrogen came from inside the boiling inferno of a supernova. Our physical body is nothing more than a complex mixture of stardust.

Many ancient mythologists recognized Mother Earth as the giver of life, Father Sun as its sustainer and provider. That's true insofar as it goes. But Father Sun is a second or third generation star himself, having come into existence only about 5 billion years ago compared to 10 to 20 billion years for the Universe. We, therefore, are the grandchildren, or great-grandchildren, of some long forgotten supernova. Our grandparent is now a neutron corpse spinning in some remote stellar cemetery.

This time consuming process hardly seems the handiwork of an impatient and careless Creator. He/She, working on a cosmic scale with microscopic bits of matter, had to have had an elegant plan. It's all too precise to be an accident. Though we have a general idea of the physics involved in Creation, the metaphysical purpose of it all remains a mystery.

This leads to other mysteries such as: how many

cycles has the Universe experienced, when and where did the first life evolve within the Universe, how many solar systems have come into being to later be fried to a crisp by a red giant, or blown to bits by a supernova? How many civilizations perished when their planet vaporized? Is Earth just one of many second or third generation planets which support life? If so, the Creator had plenty of experience when He/She seeded planet Earth with the first life forms.

Mother Earth

Father Sun, by a process not fully understood, came into being due to the gravitational attraction between gas and dust paricles emitted by a grandfather supernova.[3] It didn't take long by cosmic time standards, perhaps 500 million years or so. As gravity caused the accumulation of more and more mass, the heat of compression triggered hydrogen fusion in the core. A tiny fraction of the in-falling material failed to score a direct hit on Sun's surface but became captured by fingers of its gravitational field. These particles fell into orbit forming a disk, or number of disks, around the Sun. These rotating disks contained the source material from which Mother Earth and her sister planets formed. Smaller globules of matter came together, forming moons orbiting a hostess planet. The assembly of Mother Earth, and presumably the other planets, was essentially complete about 4.5 billion years ago.

Mother Earth resembles a living organism in that she has undergone continuous change. She suffered a violent childhood. Impacting matter scarred her face, her surface was much hotter than now, volcanos spewed molten lava and poison gas, her surface writhed and convulsed. This early geothermal activity formed a primitive atmosphere consisting primarily of methane* and some free hydrogen which has since escaped into outer space. The early atmosphere also contained small quantities of water vapor, nitrogen, some rare gases, and deadly hydrogen sulfide.

It's uncertain exactly how or when oceans began forming. Volcanic activity was more violent and frequent during Earth's early life. Since present day eruptions emit large quantities of water vapor, science postulates that volcanic activity provided the primary source of water on the planet. High clouds of dust and ash probably obscured direct sunlight much of the time which kept atmospheric temperatures low enough to allow condensation of accumulated water vapor. Torrential rains no doubt followed periods of intense volcanic activity. Ponds and lakes would form in surface depressions. In time these would merge to become warm, shallow seas. It was a slow process probably requiring a thousand million years or more.

Another Mystery—The Spark of Life

These warm ancient seas became the womb of life. Somehow, by some process we don't understand, a primitive life form was born to Mother Earth. Was it a miracle: stardust coming to life? We might think that the first living cell was merely a coincidence, a chance chemical reaction resulting from a bolt of lightning or from some other natural event. Millions of chemical reactions are possible, and given enough time, about anything might happen. Was emergent life a coincidence, an improbable event that occurred here on Earth and nowhere else in the Universe?

---

*Methane is common household gas, the same stuff we cook and heat with.

Not likely. We might wave aside the emergence of life as mere accident except for one thing. That first living cell was not immortal, and for life to continue, a succession of identical accidents are necessary. The odds against this happening are beyond calculation. Though death be an inescapable conclusion to individual life forms, nature, with its wisdom, devised a way for life to be self-perpetuating. That is, the first living cell had internal instructions which mandated the replication and division of more cells identical to itself. And the second generation of cells and all succeeding generations carried the same internal command. It isn't reasonable to think that the life force is coincidence. Life resulted from willful determination. That first living cell carried a spark of Supreme Intelligence which stipulated a long earthly mission. We can reasonably think that the same Intelligence operates throughout the Universe, hence life must abound to the farthermost corner of space.

Life, unlike cosmic events which announce each new development with an explosive fireball, sneaked in silently, unobserved, quite unpretentious. Indeed, if naked human eyes had then existed, life would have gone completely unnoticed for its first 3,000 million years of existence.

Up the Ladder of Life

It's easy to write and read a phrase containing the term *a million or billion years*, it's quite another thing to conceive how long that is in comparison to our usual concept of time. I've developed a mental game to help put cosmic and geologic time into human perspective.

Imagine that you have a stick five feet long with each inch marked like that of an ordinary yard stick.

Now mentally lean the stick against a wall with the top being point zero (present time) and 60 inches being at the floor. Each one inch subdivision represents 100 million years. The bottom of the stick therefore represents a time 6 billion years ago. If you have trouble forming a mental image of the model, turn to Fig. 2-1 at the end of the chapter.

The Big Bang occurred one or two stick lengths below the floor, so you can see that we are entering the cosmic plan relatively late. Now mentally elevate your attention upward to around inch marker 54 or 55. Here a giant star exploded in supernova creating the primal elements from which Sun, Earth, and the other planets formed. From that point up to inch marker 51 or 52 a huge nebula containing stardust began to fragment. Gravity somehow captured one of these fragments and molded it to form our Sun. At the 50 marker thermonuclear reactions erupted in its core. Excess stardust fell into orbit around the Sun, providing material for planets. Earth was essentially complete somewhere between markers 45 to 46.

On Earth, intense geothermal activity prevailed up past the 40 marker, after which it subsided sufficient to allow the first life form to sneak in somewhere between markers 35 to 40. These were simple little single cell microbes which floated around in ancient seas doing nothing more than making more and more simple cells. Improvements came slow. Not until up about marker 25 had single cell life advanced sufficiently to form soft-bodied microorganisms. The sea eventually swarmed with these tiny creatures and the first energy crunch developed at the 20 marker (existing food sources became scarce).

If you have lost track of time, we now stand at 2 billion years ago (two thousand million). Before this, the sulphur in atmospheric hydrogen sulfide provided nourishment for primitive life forms. With decreased volcanic activity and increased consumption, this source couldn't sustain the escalating abundance of life. Something had to happen, and it did. That event, or happening, introduced the oxygen revolution. This represented a major modification of the evolutionary process.

Even primitive life was resourceful, capable of controlling its environment. The solution to the energy problem involved certain organisms learning to derive energy directly from the Sun. This process (photosynthesis) survived the eons and is today the mechanism by which plants receive energy. It was a happy circumstance for those species who had developed a new method of survival. It spelled doom for the older forms.

The oxygen produced by photosynthesis was toxic to many of the older organisms. They simply went into extinction when oxygen began to collect in the atmosphere. It accumulated slowly because much competition exists for oxygen. It is a very congenial element. It likes to join with metals to form oxides, with carbon and calcium to form limestone and dolomite rocks, with silicon to form granite, and with carbon alone to form carbon monoxide (CO which is toxic to respiratory creatures) and carbon dioxide (CO_2), the chief nutrient of plant life. Its affinity toward other elements consumed 99.99% of its total earthly supply. The remaining 0.01% is available for breathing. Most of this now comes as a waste product from plant life with lesser amounts released during photolysis (the reaction occurring from ultraviolet radiation splitting water molecules to form ozone (O_3), free oxygen (O_2), and free hydrogen which escapes Earth's atmosphere).

Oxygen, though it be an absolute necessity for

breathing creatures, serves another critical role in support of biological systems. When combined with hydrogen it forms water (H_2O). Not one single life form on Earth could exist without water in liquid form. We are all aqueous creatures. Even though the ancestors of land dwelling creatures crawled up on dry land several hundred million years ago, their bodies, as does ours, contained about 85% saline water.

Single cell life forms slowly became more sophisticated. At about marker 10, cells began to coalesce which announced the coming reign of multicellular life. This was another breakthrough for evolving life. By now the naked eye might detect a blue-green tint in placid bays and shallow water.* Oxygen production increased dramatically which triggered many changes upon the surface of Mother Earth. Comparatively speaking, multicellular life prompted an explosion in both the size and diversification of species.

Increased oxygen in the atmosphere altered the land portion of Mother Earth through a process of rock weathering by oxidation, which in turn led to deposition of altered rock strata in regions of low elevation (sedimentation). This process of weathering and sedimentation due to wind and rain is still active today. Geologists divide the age of sedimentation into several periods. Each of these periods display distinctive geologic conditions and unique biological characteristics. It is impossible to cram all of this information into the top six inches of our imaginary stick. Therefore, re-calibrate your imagination so that one inch now equals 10 million years; that is, the top of the stick is present time, the bottom a time 600 million years ago. If you are following Fig. 2-1, shift your attention to Fig. 2.2.

---

*This would be an accumulation of algae, a primitive plant form still in existence.

If naked eyes were waiting patiently to see an example of this thing called life, finally after some 3,000 million years, their reward came in Cambrian times (marker 57 to just below marker 50). The sea still swarmed with plankton and microbial life but one would also see small worm-like creatures, jellyfish, and small shell-covered critters scampering across the ocean floor. They would appear somewhat like a many-legged beetle except larger. If curious naked eyes had gazed toward land their owners would gasp in horror at seeing the desolate terrain: no grass, no plants, no trees, no life. It might look like the lunar landscape except that a violent dust storm might sweep by. The land surface would show scars of erosion with gullies and deep canyons pointing toward the sea. A Cambrian beach was no place for a Sunday picnic.

The Ordovician period, between markers 44 to 50, brought a wider variety of life into the marine system. Life in general was increasing in body size and complexity. The oceans sheltered mollusks, star fish, sea urchins, and a host of shell fish. By the close of this period large predators the size of modern day dolphins terrorized smaller species. Also, a few hardy species of plants invaded land to splash green over Mother Earth's terrestrial regions. Then came the Silurian, the relatively short interval between markers 41 to 44. The early part of this period witnessed the recovery of marine life which had suffered mass extinctions during the late Ordovician. Sea life continued to grow in body size and becme more diversified, and aggressive.

A radical innovation in life forms occurred during the late Devonian, between markers 36 to 41. Fierce sea predators had become even larger. They also had an internal skeleton which made them swift and more agile despite increasing body size.[4] The terrestrial landscape was also improving: large freshwater swamps crept inland, forests of tall coniferous trees provided shelter from the incessant wind. Perhaps to escape the terrors at sea, a few of the smaller vertebrate species crawled up on dry land to there eke out an existence. Some lapped up insects which were also new, others browsed in the swamps. Life on land was tranquil compared to that in the oceans.

Amphibians, though increasingly becoming land dwellers, had to return to water to lay their eggs. Reptilian creatures breached this handicap during late Carboniferous times (markers 29 to 36) by depositing eggs on dry land. No longer was emergent life dependent upon the sea for survival. Lush forests with dense undergrowth flourished through this time. Dead trees and plants would fall and another growth would take their place. In time, thick beds of organic matter accumulated to later become covered with land sediments. These deposits now constitute most of the world's coal supply. Small reptiles resembling today's lizards also flourished. Like life at sea, reptiles slowly gained body size. Some were browsers, others ate insects and small creatures.

Moving upward into Permian and Triassic times (markers 21 to 29), reptiles continued their ascendancy, becoming sovereign rulers over the terrestrial terrain. To peer over this landscape with naked human eyes would be both awesome and frightening. The dinosaurs had arrived. They were the largest creatures ever to walk the surface of Mother Earth. Some were meek browsers who munched lush foliage; others were agile and fierce predators. Large flying reptiles with a wingspan up to 40 feet swooped from the sky to devour unsuspecting prey. If one found themselves in this scene, he or she would surely look for a hole in which to hide. And that's exactly what mammals, our earliest ancestors, did. The first true mammals were quite small, resembling modern day rodents. They were probably nocturnal ground burrowing creatures, and they were certainly out of place—big was the order of the times, big predators dominated the sea, big reptiles ruled the land. It was no place for man to stake out a homestead.

The climate was mild through Jurassic and Cretaceous times (markers 6½ to 21), but it still wasn't a time or place to plant corn fields. In fact, not until the middle Cretaceous did flowering plants and deciduous trees appear on land. But even if corn had then existed, we would need some mighty high fences to prevent the dinosaurs from trampling our fields. No, this was the undisputed kingdom of reptiles, a few of which evolved into the first true birds having feathers.

Though not shown on Figures 2-1, 2-2, or 2-3, nor chronologically positioned on our mental model, dynamic geologic events had profound effects upon evolving life. Continental drift, more properly termed plate tectonics, continually altered Earth's geography. Simply said, each continent rests on a plate which drifts around on the crust of Mother Earth. In times past all the continents lay snuggled together forming one huge super-continent. This may be the reason why similar fossils exist on continents which are now far removed. At present, the continents lay widely dispersed with each having its own distinctive life forms. Continents sometimes rip apart, forming a rift (valley), sometimes they collide with mountain building force. The mighty Himalayas, the Alps, the Andes, and the Coastal range on the Pacific coast of North America are recent examples.

Since continents move more less at random, places

which are now tropical once lay over one of the arctic poles; conversely, regions of high or low latitude were once tropical. Meandering continents have therefore undergone a wide variety of climatic conditions. Plant and animal life suffers severe stress when a tropical zone becomes temperate and finally arctic. Many species die, new species having the ability to survive in an altered environment take their place. Changing climate due to drifting continents took a toll both on land and at sea.

The near simultaneous death of many species goes under the term *mass extinction.* But here we need an understanding of simultaneous as used in the preceding context. Remember, we are dealing with geologic time, with one inch on our mental stick equal to 10 million years. As an example, suppose that a continent centered over the equator began moving south at the rate of two inches per year. After 27 million years, it would center over the South Pole. That represents one-fourth inch on our first mental stick (Fig. 2-1), about 2¾ inches on the second stick (Fig. 2-2). Palm trees can't exist in arctic regions. Neither can other tropical species, including marine life. In all probability, most would perish long before reaching latitude 45 degrees south. Therefore, as we view time, most mass extinctions probably occurred over an extended period.

Drifting continents were just one of many possible factors contributing to mass extinctions (ice ages and varying climate, for examples). Several mass extinctions appear on Fig. 2-2 because they fit the graphics, many others don't fit in. Those shown represent a mere sampling because paleontologists think that perhaps as many as twenty extinctions occurred during the history of life.

Probably the most known and widely publicized

mass extinction occurred at the end of Cretaceous time some 66 million years ago. The dinosaurs suffered extinction during this episode. The cause of this great dying is the subject of considerable study, and debate. Substantial evidence is accumulating which suggests that a large meteor struck Earth at that time. The impact hurled huge clouds of dust and ash into the upper atmosphere which obscured the Sun for several years before settling.* Large cold blooded creatures were particularly vulnerable to extended artificial winter conditions. But reptiles were not solitary victims, many other species on land and at sea also succumbed. Whatever the cause, small mammals were the principal survivors.

Land areas became strangely quiet and serene following the exodus of large reptiles at the close of Cretaceous time (marker 6.5). The small surviving mammals came from underground, and seeing a calm setting, they remained on the surface. They suffered little competition and encountered few predators. It was time for warm blood creatures to gain dominance over the land. Their anatomy permitted survival during periods of cooler climates because of an insulating fur coat and a metabolic system capable of maintaining constant body temperature.

Beginning in the Paleogene (marker 6.5) and extending upward into the late Neogene (about 1/2" from the top of our mental stick) mammal species began a hurried scramble up the Ladder of Life. Following the example established by reptiles, mammals became increasingly large and more complex. Whales, the largest living mammal today, evolved early in the period. By about 35 million years ago, giant pigs, rhinocer-

---

*If this was the cause, it represents simultaneous extinction in the strictest sense.

oses, hyenas, saber-toothed cats, and the forerunners of many modern species roamed the continents. Primates (monkeys), mankind's earliest cousin, arrived about 24 million years ago (marker 2.4). Adding a note of cheer to an increasingly hostile environment, small nonaggressive song birds glided over a changing landscape.

Plant life also flourished during the Neogene. The first grasses spread across previously barren land. Included within this family are the grains from which we make bread and breakfast cereal. Herbs and weeds also arrived at this time; we may abhor dandelions and other irksome plants, but consider that our vegetables and spices also come from this family. The terrestrial terrain of six million years ago would appear vaguely familiar—fruit trees, blooming plants, waving grass, dense forests of hardwood and coniferous trees, chirping birds, crawling bugs, and herds of animals who were the primitive cousins of today's animal kingdom.

We will now concentrate on the emergence of mankind. To do so, we must again re-calibrate our five foot stick. This time each inch equals 100,000 years, with the bottom of the stick being six million years ago. Those following Fig. 2-2 should shift attention to Fig. 2-3.

The footprints of emergent man lead back to east-central Africa.[5] It was here that at least two species of pre-human species originated. Not much is known about Ramapithecus and Gigantopithecus. Paleontologists infer, from the few fossils found thus far, that they were neither apes nor hominids (two-legged). They think that these forerunners of man evolved, not in the jungle, but on the open savannah which represents a major departure from tradition within the higher primate family. Their age and tenure is uncertain with suggestions of origin ranging from 10 to 15 million years ago. They both fell into extinction some 5 to 8 million years back. Neither species are particularly important to our understanding of the ascent of man other than they represent the first sprout of a new branch of life within the higher primate family.

More hard data exists for Australopithecus. It's not certain when they first appeared although some anthropologists speculate that they arrived between 4 to 5 million years ago (between markers 40 to 50). The original stock divided into four different subspecies (afarensis, africanus, robustus, and boisei). Australopithecus went into extinction as late as 1.2 million years ago (marker 12). Their physical stature was relatively small, an adult standing about 4 feet tall. Their brain was much smaller than ours but the evidence clearly suggests that they walked fully upright—this in contrast to apes and chimps who knuckle walk (use an upper limb as a sort of crutch). Other evidence suggests that by about 3.5 million years ago Australopithecus practiced monogamy with both mates and offspring living together as a family unit, thus establishing the first elements of culture. The exact cause of their extinction is unknown although some think they succumbed due to competition from advanced species.

Homo habilis arrived about 2 million years ago (perhaps earlier), then fell into extinction about a half-million or so years later (marker 15). He was no larger than Austra man but nature bestowed upon him two new and very important improvements. His brain was larger, and to accompany higher intellect, his thumbs twisted inward to oppose the index fingers (like our hands). This allowed precision grip of small objects. Handy hands, from the Latin word *habilis*, gave him the reputation of being the world's first tool maker. Homo habilis didn't last long by biological standards (around 500,000 years), albeit, he survived some 5 to 8 times longer than modern man's present tenure. He did hand those handy hands forward to Homo erectus and all subsequent hominid species.

Almost immediately, if not before, Homo erectus stepped in to fill the vacancy left by Homo habilis. It's possible that Homo erectus created the vacancy because of his increased intellect and improved anatomy which overwhelmed the smaller and more cumbersome Homo habilis. It's also possible that Homo erectus experienced the world's first population explosion. For whatever reason, he wasn't content with life in Africa and began migrating northward into Europe and Asia. He reached northern China some half-million years ago, then crossed the equator to far away Indonesia (Java). His remnants found in China appear to be at an encampment where charcoal (ashes) and animal bones littered the floor of a cave. This leads to speculation that Homo erectus knew how to control fire (marker 5).

Fire was essential to the survival of those first northern pioneers. The northern hemisphere suffered repeated glaciation during the ascent of Homo species. Huge ice sheets spread south of the arctic region to cover large segments of northern Europe, Asia, and North America. Intermittent periods of global warming sent the ice back toward the polar region. Emergent man, and the herds upon which he depended, vacillated north and south with each change in climatic conditions. Even during warm periods, such as the present, man can't survive winter in the higher latitudes without a hearth.

Erectus was quite successful—he lasted until about 300,000 years ago (marker 3) before surrendering his domains to yet another improved species. Homo sapiens (wise man), our immediate ancestor, had a brain even larger than ours, a physique which would be the envy of every linebacker in the National Football League, and a tool kit of some 60 utility instruments. The most famous of this species was Neanderthal man who centered a high culture in southwestern Europe from about 125,000 years ago until his demise about 35,000 years ago.

Here We Stand—Doing Symphonies and Immortal Art

It's a matter of some conjecture regarding when modern man first came on the scene. Some say about 40,000 years ago, others think he may have arrived earlier than 100,000 years ago. Compromising the disparity, we will arbitrarily draw a line on our mental stick about a half-inch from the top. We do know that a high culture called Cro-Magnon society settled in Neanderthal's territory about 35 to 40 thousand years ago to there found an advanced culture. It was a time of global warming with the last ice cap withdrawing toward the arctic, reaching its present position about 10,000 years ago. Then hunter-gatherer societies began to yield ground when agriculture first appeared in the Middle East some 6 to 8 thousand years ago.

What about the first symphony? First, come down from the top of the stick a distance equal to the thickness of this page: that's when Moses wrote his version of Creation as recorded in Genesis. Now, move 5/6 of that distance back toward the top of the stick: that's when Shakespeare wrote his classics and Leonardo da Vinci painted the Mona Lisa. Up slightly from here is where Bach composed a symphony.

Our tenure on Earth is so brief compared to other species that future archaeologists may completely overlook our existence; or at best, consider us a temporary transitional species announcing *Homo super sapiens*. Despite our late arrival, and without due regard for our limited experience, the Western tradition still maintains that the Creator bestowed upon man dominion over the fishes in the sea, birds in the air, and animals on the land. This seems a rather odd notion. Life floated and crawled around on the surface of Mother Earth for some 3½ to 4 billion years without any help from mankind. Millions upon millions of species have come and gone during that time. Who was their guardian?—certainly not man. Considering that Moses wasn't privy to modern day knowledge when he composed Genesis, his error is understandable. What's inexcusable is the tenacity with which we cling to a tradition giving mankind license to sacrifice other species for his material gain.

Excepting intelligence, creative consciousness, and a body designed to perform intricate tasks, man isn't basically much different from other life forms. We come from stardust, the same stuff from which mountains and moons are made. But we are unique with respect to ability. No species, save one, can write or conduct a symphony. How is it that man, a single species among millions, is capable of composing a symphony?*

We need not feel smug concerning our abilities. The secret of our success came implanted within the first microbe to arrive on Mother Earth. The vehicle of evolution lays coiled in a single molecule known as DNA. From that humble fragment of intelligence grew ever more sophisticated life forms. We just

---

*Birds are an exception in that they not only do melody, they learn songs from other birds—but they are yet to create classic art or literature.

happen to be the first species (on Earth anyway) having the ability to capitalize upon a process that contains an inherent urge to ever strive toward a higher purpose. Symphonies arise due to a built-in predisposition leading toward more complex self-organization. Inherent within the system is a potential for thinking, reasoning, a conscious realization that one is alive. Symphonies are the result of creative consciousness, an ability made possible by imbuing inorganic matter with intellectual intent.

Great. But this is hardly a profound conclusion. It's merely recognition of a process which started some 3 to 4 billion years ago. The fundamental question is: from whence came that initial spark of intelligence? A special gift bestowed by the Creator? Or, do we err in assuming that inorganic matter is devoid of intelligence?

Consider this: at the present stage of cosmic evolution the four known forces of physics consistently produce predictable results. Gravity never allows planet Earth to wander from its orbit around the Sun, we always receive uninterrupted radiation from the never failing thermonuclear reactor which supplies all our energy. Chemical reactions involving inorganic matter repeat with monotonous regularity. An obscure intelligence appears to exist at subatomic levels; that is, in particle physics two virtual particles separated by space seem to know exactly what the other is doing at all times. Even abstract principles hold true—two and two always stack up to four. We're left to speculate: is there any fundamental difference between organic and inorganic matter? Or more precisely, is all matter right down to the smallest particle under the influence of a cosmic energy field having intelligence and consciousness?

Now it seems we have come full circle back to our original questions. To hypothesize the existence of an as yet unidentified life carrying energy field is an expression of ignorance not much better than a mythology which portrays an omnipotent creator breathing life into a handful of dust. Either account implies Supreme Intelligence. Both incorporate a process which transcends human perception. So, whether we defend an ancient myth or labor with microscopes, the source of the spark of life remains metaphysical.

The evolutionary process is dynamic and ever ongoing. Mother Earth and Father Sun are only halfway through their expected longevity. The process will continue, to where we know not. If the past is an indication of the future, we could reasonably predict higher and more advanced life forms to emerge from the rubble of obsolete species which pass into extinction. To think that mankind, species *Homo sapien sapien*, represents an end-point, the final summit of biological evolution, is to indulge in sanctimonious chauvinism. The process that brought life to planet Earth is certainly more elegant than anything we can imagine or mentally concoct.

The source of life remains hidden, a mystery known only to the Creator. Nonetheless, following the footprints of evolving life on planet Earth is a mystic journey, a sensing of the love and compassion of our Creator. Only enough is revealed to further excite our curiosity. Legends of old or esoteric tales of extraterrestrials peopling Earth all pale before the beauty and majesty of cosmic evolution, of swirling galaxies and orbiting solar systems, of colliding continents and rising mountains, of emergent life with its persistence, diversity, and adaptability as revealed by rocks of the ages. Mother Earth shelters and preserves these imbedded fossils because they contain Her immortal secrets, Her life history. The intelligence, perseverance, and adaptability of life is truly a miracle far surpassing anything devised by the mind of man.

Fig. 2-1, turn page

Introduction to the Ladder of Life

When I was young and living in Colorado I sometimes climbed up to the high outcrops which rimmed the valley through which my favorite river flowed. One day I noticed what looked like a snail shell imbedded into what I now know was a shale formation overlaid by a 50 to 60 foot sandstone member. I thought that rather unusual, so using a rock I carefully chipped it out and brought it home. Neither Dad nor anybody else could explain how it got there. Further explorations yielded a cluster of such shells cemented by a white chalky substance. I later found the imprint of a leaf some 2½" to 3 inches long. My questions produced a lot of shrugs, but finally one well intentioned person suggested that these fossils were washed high up on the mountain during Noah's flood. I remained a skeptic because I couldn't understand how a flood could push snails and leaves into solid rock.

Unknown to me at the time, naturalists in Europe had asked these same questions of themselves several centuries earlier. They proposed several theories including one of sedimentation, but given established orthodoxy, their theories failed for lack of sufficient time. Further evidence began to provide overwhelming confirmation of a much older Earth, not the least of which was the finding of fossils having no resemblance to present day species. These naturalists eventually backed from beneath the shadow of theology and the science of geology became an established discipline.

Paleontology is a branch of geology which specializes in the study of fossils. Had I then known a present day paleontologist, he or she could have given me a name for my snail shells, their approximate age, and described the process of how they came to be there. They could also have identified the leaf imprint and told me the species of plant from which it had fallen.

Paleontologists, biologists, and anthropologists have devised ingenious methods to determine the time when various fossils were deposited. Most of these methods rely upon measuring the decay of trace radioactive elements contained within the fossil. Accuracy diminishes with increasing age. That is, the older a fossil be, the less accurate its age can be deduced. However, as the data bank expands, the age of certain fossils can be inferred by correlation with other information.

The dates shown on the following timetable generally follow those given by Steven M. Stanley in *Earth and Life Through Time*.[6] Experts don't always agree on dates and classification, therefore some of the data is compromised using the work of other authors. The fact remains, the ages shown are approximations at best, albeit, based upon extensive research.

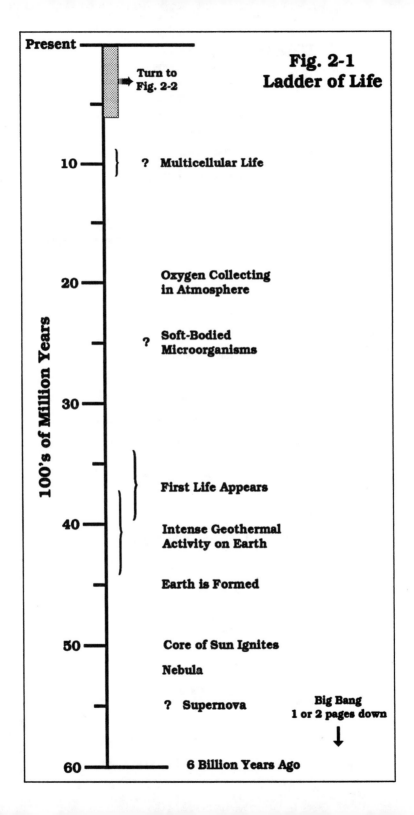

Fig. 2-1
Ladder of Life

Present

Turn to Fig. 2-2

10 — } ? Multicellular Life

20 — Oxygen Collecting in Atmosphere

? Soft-Bodied Microorganisms

30 —

First Life Appears

40 — Intense Geothermal Activity on Earth

Earth is Formed

50 — Core of Sun Ignites

Nebula

? Supernova

Big Bang 1 or 2 pages down ↓

60 — 6 Billion Years Ago

100's of Million Years

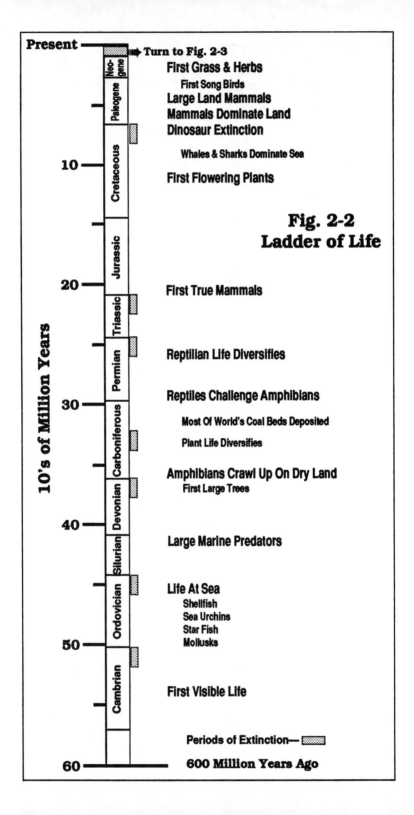

Fig. 2-2
Ladder of Life

Present ⟶ Turn to Fig. 2-3

First Grass & Herbs

First Song Birds

Large Land Mammals

Mammals Dominate Land

Dinosaur Extinction

Whales & Sharks Dominate Sea

First Flowering Plants

First True Mammals

Reptilian Life Diversifies

Reptiles Challenge Amphibians

Most Of World's Coal Beds Deposited

Plant Life Diversifies

Amphibians Crawl Up On Dry Land

First Large Trees

Large Marine Predators

Life At Sea
Shellfish
Sea Urchins
Star Fish
Mollusks

First Visible Life

Periods of Extinction— ▨

600 Million Years Ago

10's of Million Years

Present, 10, 20, 30, 40, 50, 60

Neo-gene, Paleogene, Cretaceous, Jurassic, Triassic, Permian, Carboniferous, Devonian, Silurian, Ordovician, Cambrian

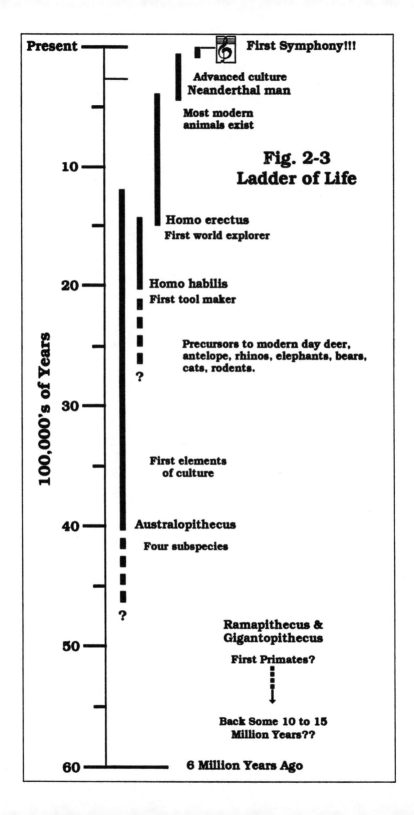

> *Time goes around and comes around, and it's not the same everywhere all the time.*

Chapter Three

TIME:

An Absolute Quantity or an Illusion?

Who, back in yesteryear, would attach any mystery to the properties of time? We all learned how to tell-time long before starting school; merely glancing at the hands on a clock told us all we needed to know. There's nothing mysterious about time, so we thought.

The Conventional View of Time

Complying with our conventional view of time, industrial societies regulate every activity, every intention and plan, in strict accordance with the motion of hands on a clock or watch. We quit at another predetermined time. We receive wages according to the number of hours worked. We break for lunch at a certain time, we go to bed by the clock, we wake up to the offensive ring of an alarm. We count off the days toward weekends, to holidays, to vacation, to opening of fishing season, to when the semester ends, to retirement. We become so preoccupied with future time that we seldom take time to appreciate today.

In today's fast moving society time is a commodity,

something measured out in small parcels, something others are always demanding from us. We are stingy with time. Its limited availability requires that we establish priorities, that we neglect some things while concentrating on others. People write books and give lectures on how to manage time; but in truth, we don't manage time—it manipulates us.

It hasn't always been this way. In the last chapter we nonchalantly marked off time in increments of millions and billions of years. The Cambrian, a period more than 500 million years ago, seemed relatively recent in the unfolding saga of emergent life. Modern civilization arrived on Earth such a short time ago that man's accomplishments are scarcely more than the width of a pencil line on the Ladder of Life.

Early man didn't think about minutes and hours and days. He regulated his life by the seasons; he scheduled his activities by the moon and/or celestial events such as the equinoxes. There was a season for hunting, for gathering, for planting, for harvest; and in later times, a season for warfare.* Meals didn't come according to schedule; people ate when they either found something edible, bagged game, discovered plunder. Neither did they sleep on schedule; they rested only after filling their stomach and finding a safe haven from predators. They didn't divide the day into 24 hour increments; a day constituted sunrise to sunrise. It was a success if one survived.

Seconds, minutes, and hours became important only after mankind became secure within warm shelters with a steady supply of provisions. And an uninterrupted stream of supplies increasingly involved trans-

---

*Before invention of the wheel, a soldier's provisions were what he could carry on his back. Therefore, invasions took place after harvest so one's army could subsist bv plunder.

portation in some form. Ships between ports brought goods from distant lands, carts and wagons carried food from the country to cities. Transportation became increasingly complex as Europe entered the industrial era: ores, coal, timber, and other resources flowed inward to the factory, finished products flowed outward to the consumer. Scheduling became ever more complicated. This required the standardization of time. And, for things to run smoothly, it had to be the same time everywhere to meet schedules and deadlines. We've contended with schedules and deadlines ever since.

Our quantification of time prompts us to treat it like a tangible asset. We come to think of time as a checking account which we inherit at birth. The problem associated with this sort of time accounting is that we never know the initial or remaining balance. We do acknowledge that each of us receive a finite quantity of time. We are born at a specific time, our time will terminate at some future point. Our personal experience is that time has a beginning and an ending. We therefore tend to view nature in the same context; there must be a start and end for all things.

This infatuation with quantified time is what causes us to look backward toward origins—to sneak a peek into the records to discover the beginning balance of our time account. If we know the original balance, and since the passage of quantified time is measurable, we might then be able to predict some future terminal event. This obsession with time is what Chapter One was about. Cosmologists consider the start of time as coincident with the Big Bang. If the Universe closes, time will expire at the Big Crunch. If the Universe is open, the effect on time will be something like old soldiers, "it won't die, it will just fade away."

The Mythological Dilemma Concerning Time

The start of time presents an enigma: what came before time? It's difficult to imagine a time when time didn't exist, never existed. And once started, now can time end? Yes, our personal allotment can expire, but time itself, how can it end? By reaching some terminal event such as the Big Crunch?

If the Big Crunch does indeed result in the end of time, we become looked into finite time. But, if time has a beginning and an end, can there be such a thing as eternity?

Creation via the will of an intelligent and all powerful deity is a convenient idea because it sidesteps some otherwise troubling problems. However, if nothing existed, and if time was still an egg waiting to hatch, where, when, and how did a *physical* creator come into being? If nothing existed before the beginning, and if time was dormant, and if man is the image of a physical creator, logic would tell us that creation is impossible.

When I was young they all said that the Creator has always been, an eternal presence. This presented a mental dilemma because I couldn't envision *eternity*, particularly the idea of eternal damnation. In retrospect, it's obvious that my mentors also had a problem with time because eternity seems to imply infinite time, without beginning, without end. This would negate their source of authority, "In the *beginning* God created the heaven and earth," where heaven is presumed the celestial home of a physical creator.

A beginning, or first cause, suggests the start of time; but no, they said that the Creator is eternal which again brings us back to infinite time. Therefore, if time is infinite, and heaven and earth are temporal, where was the Creator before He/She created heaven? And another nagging question, why during infinite time did the Creator wait so long before creating heaven and earth?

Perhaps we could think of time as finite having come into existence at the moment of Creation, and the Creator as a Spirit having no physical characteristics. Spirit would then become nothing more than consciousness, a thinking creative cosmic mind. This would resolve the dilemma associated with the absence of matter. But what about time? If there was no time before Creation, Spirit would exist in a state of animated suspension—immobile, with consciousness frozen into a stationary state. With consciousness suspended there could be no thinking and no creative planning. Without time's existence, the deity itself must come into being simultaneous with Creation, in which case the deity was not the Creator, regarding time at least.

We could resolve this conflict in rationale by presuming that somehow time pre-existed the instant of Creation. But again, this contradicts the opening line of Genesis, "In the *beginning...*" Furthermore, to assume that time pre-existed Creation would imply the presence of two creators, one who made time, one who created the Universe. Two creators! Such a statement four centuries ago would have earned me the dubious honor of being the central guest at a burning stake ceremony. This is not only heresy, it also is illogical because from whence came the first creator?

The Mathematical Paradox Concerning Time

The problem of time puzzles many thinkers. Is time a reality or merely a reference point, or both? For instance, we are born at a precise moment in history, but is this simply a point where we step onto the wheel of life? Does the passage of years since birth represent the forward march of time, or does it depict a journey around the circle of life? Our death will also be another precise moment in history, but will it be the end of time as we know it or just another reference point where we step off the merry-go-round of earthly life? Is the arrow of time an illusion, a convenient way to mark a continuous succession of reference points? Taking a pragmatic view of time, someone once said, "time is what keeps everything from happening all at once."[1]

The twentieth century toppled many previous concepts of time. As noted earlier, at the turn of this century most laymen believed Earth to be about 6,000 years old. This number came from the seventeenth century Biblical chronology determined by James Ussher (and duplicated by others). Ussher, the Archbishop of Armagh, using the genealogy of Biblical characters in the Old Testament, calculated 4,004 B.C. as the date of Creation. Lacking any other authentic evidence, the laity had little reason to question the age of Mother Earth. Ussher's work went unchallenged because little knowledge of natural history was then available— geologists, physicists, and biologists came later. Moreover, at this point in history scientific ideas were of little interest to the public at large.

The public remained largely apathetic toward science even as Europe entered the Industrial Age. However, science began blooming as the wheels of industry turned ever faster. Naturalists chipped fossil specimens from the Earth, astronomers defined the solar system, physicists discovered the mechanics of moving bodies. Then Charles Darwin threw Ussher's timetable into disarray when he published the *Origin of Species*. The church was aghast at such a proposal, but not so with naturalists. Several concurred with his theory of biological evolution and it soon became apparent that such a process would require hundreds of thousands of years. Science was ready to accept the idea of a much older Earth because it gave latitude to confirm observations. The study of earth science accelerated, the boundaries of biology expanded, the study of physics escalated.

Darwin lifted the time restraints imposed by theology, budding geology continually pushed back the time of Earth's origin. Evolving physics introduced another paradox concerning the nature of time.

Isaac Newton published *Mathematical Principles of Natural Philosophy* in 1687, nearly two centuries before Darwin published his work. Newton's work earned him the reputation of having invented calculus and becoming the father of modern physics. Included in the work are three Laws of Motion which still form the foundation of conventional physics. These Laws, and also Einstein's equations relating to general relativity, interject another interesting paradox concerning the nature of time: their equations work equally well if we reverse the direction of time. It makes no difference whether time proceeds into the future, or whether it retreats into the past.

Consider Newton's Second Law of Motion: acceleration is one of three variables which enter into the equation.[2] Time enters the parameters defining acceleration twice, meaning a multiplication of itself (time squared). You will recall from algebra that two negative numbers multiplied together will yield a positive product. Therefore, negative time squared comes out positive. The resultant force comes out positive regardless of which way time flows.

Most physicists and philosophers take mathematics serious. Some honestly question the forward march of time (frequently termed, The Arrow of Time). Others advance a lengthy defense for the Arrow of Time.[3] A popular analogy supporting the irreversible nature of time goes something like: you never see a bull backing into a china shop, repairing the wreckage, then backing out leaving an orderly display of wares.

Most of us don't hold mathematics in high enough regard to accept reversible time, personal experience supersedes abstract principles. But if we reject what mathematics tells us concerning time, can we be certain that two plus two will always stack up to four? Either something is wrong with mathematics (doubtful), or the properties of time are variable.

Variable Time

Isaac Newton put a tip on both ends of the Arrow of Time. Darwin stretched time beyond human perception. Albert Einstein further distorted our concept of time. His equations of special and general relativity not only confirm Nelson's reversible time, he also said that time was a component of space, that the two are inseparable. Moreover, his theory of general relativity states that gravity warps and bends spacetime. Warped space, relative time! What's this all about?

There's neither enough space nor time to here discuss the two theories of relativity (the theory of special relativity came in 1905, general relativity came in 1915). Furthermore, it's reminiscent of a passage contained in Julian Schwinger's book, *Einstein's Legacy: The Unity of Space and Time*.[4] Wrote Schwinger, quoting a chemist who accompanied Einstein on a boat trip to the United States in 1921, "Einstein explained his theory to me every day, and on my arrival I was fully convinced that he understood it." After reading Schwinger's book, and several others relating to the subject, I am fully convinced that some scientists understand relativity.

I don't pretend to understand the mathematics behind relativity. The entire theory transcends common sense; it provides predictions which are extremely difficult, if not impossible, to conceive. At best, I can only describe some of the implications as they relate to time, these coming from physicists who claim an understanding of relativity.

First, we are told that gravity effects what we may call the passing of time; that is, the stronger the field of gravity, the faster a clock will run. This means that time in outer space, where gravity is *relatively* weak, will pass slower than observed by a person on Earth. Taken to the extreme and other things not considered, we could speculate that in the complete absence of gravity time would stretch into eternity. But it doesn't happen because other things must be considered (spacetime, discussed in the next sub-section).

Furthermore, motion also effects time. That is, the faster an object moves, its time of travel decreases relative to the lapse of time recorded by a stationary observer. Taken to the extreme, if we accelerated our watch to the speed of light, its time would appear to stand still if we could see its face. Unfortunately, we couldn't see the face of our watch because the light reflected from its face couldn't get back to us. Moreover, it's impossible for any object larger than a photon to achieve the speed of light. It's possible to accelerate subatomic particles to a speed approaching that of light, but an amazing thing happens. The faster an object moves, the more massive it becomes (when time stretches, space shrinks). Again taken to the extreme, if someone accelerated you to the speed of light (impossible) the process would require infinite energy and your total mass would exceed that contained in the entire Universe.

Strange concepts indeed, is Einstein mistaken?

All new theories of science must stand the test of experiment, and if they fail to produce the predicted results, or if other scientists can't duplicate the experiment, the theory loses credence. Einstein had plenty of critics. His equations are difficult to understand, satisfactory experimental techniques were yet unknown. Given these problems, the idea of relativity was slow to gain acceptance even within scientific circles.

Science itself was undergoing a major transformation at the time. As Einstein probed the vast expanse of the Universe, other physicists were investigating the microscopic realm of particle physics. Though at first appearing unrelated, the two disciplines of science aided and abetted one another in a curious way. Einstein's special theory of relativity equated energy with mass.[5] It also states that light consists of a stream of photons (the smallest possible particle) and that nothing can ever surpass the speed of a photon. This new concept, together with emerging particle physics, provided physicists the ability to *split the atom.* We are too familiar with the results—the atomic bomb (atomic fission rather than fusion as in the hydrogen bomb). Thereafter, with expanding experience and technology, physicists came to understand Einstein and to think of experimental ways to test general relativity.

Atomic clocks were in operation by the time of Einstein's death in 1955. Nothing exceeds their precision. They can tell time to within a billionth of a second. Given such accuracy, scientists were able to test the time concepts predicted by general relativity.

Several experiments during the 1960s and 1970s involved atomic clocks in airplanes.[6] One test involved an aircraft circling Washington, DC, at an altitude of 30,000 feet. The intent of the experiment was to detect the effect on time caused by decreased gravity, if any. Sure enough, the atomic clock in the plane lost time compared to an identical clock on the ground. Einstein, now dead several years, came through this test and four more repeats with substantial credibility.

Another experiment, using two jet liners, involved carrying atomic clocks around the world. The purpose of this test was to determine the effect of motion on time. One flew east going with Earth's rotation which increased its speed (relative to the Universe). The other airplane went west. The atomic clock in the eastbound plane recorded less elapsed time than an identical clock stationed at the home base. The westbound plane, flying against Earth's rotation and therefore moving slower than home base, gained time relative to the other plane and also home base. The predictions of relativity held true in both instances.

Time As A Physical Substance

Einstein destroyed all previous concepts of time. We must accept that spacetime is real, and that time is not the same everywhere in the Universe. Time is not constant and durable, the effects of motion, gravity, and the location of the one who is an observer alter its properties.

The theories of relativity transcend common sense. They stand in opposition to what we think we see and experience. The cause of this seeming disparity involves the enormity of space and the limits of human perception. We can't differentiate time to billionths of a second, Earth appears quite large to our way of thinking. However, time, if stretched to encompass the Universe, becomes an inseparable component of space itself.

According to relativity, time is neither an absolute quantity nor is it an illusion. Since general relativity integrates time and space having a single physical identity known as spacetime, time cannot exist without space. And space cannot exist without time. Time is a physical substance, as is space, as is energy and matter. When space vanishes, so does time and energy and matter. Time is a property which exists only in the physical realm. And of course, gravity always effects spacetime thus preventing time stretching into eternity as speculated several paragraphs back.

It's therefore meaningless to ask what come before time. We don't ask, "which came first, energy or matter?" because we now know that both are the same.* Nothing physical existed before Creation, including time. With this question resolved, we can also eliminate the pre-creation existence of a physical creator. Such a concept violates all physical laws governing space, matter, and time.

A Transcendent Realm?

With a closed Universe, space and time will cease at the final stage of a Big Crunch. All physical things will collapse into singularity—poof, gone, disappeared. Perhaps another Big Bang will restore a similar universe at some point during ensuing eternity. If the Universe expands into a heat death as with the open model, spacetime will stretch into featureless fragments of

---

*The theory of special relativity equates matter and energy.

cold, dead, inert matter. As the final dying gasp snuffs the last shred of physical activity from the Universe, the physical properties of time and space will simply retreat into total chaos.

If any explanation exists concerning the mystery surrounding the Initial Condition, it slumbers in the vast expanse of eternity. Perhaps the mystery shrouding the Initial Condition resides in the Mind of the Creator, it being a reflection of His/Her intent; the First Cause may be an act of will on His/Her part.

*Mother Nature is wise
and shrewd, a gentle companion,
a compassionate counselor.*

Chapter Four

SILENT MESSENGERS

The Subtle Intelligence of Nature

Two months of hard winter begin to wear on one's good nature. Missing the sunshine, growing weary of shoveling snow, one begins longing for spring with its warm days and budding life.

So imagine my delight, and stirring hopes, when out the window I saw a robin perched on the deck railing. He was puffed up looking more like a porcupine than a bird. Surely, he made a mistake by returning so early. Then I saw his lady, hunched up and miserable as she clung to a branch of a big fir tree outside my window. It seemed inappropriate that these lovers should select my locale to celebrate Valentine's Day. They should have still been down in southern Colorado or Utah, or wherever they winter.

Then a couple of days later another pair arrived. All four birds pecked and scratched the frozen soil on a windswept ridge not far from the house in what was surely a vain effort. Still, it was encouraging, a faint glimmer of hope that winter was about over? My hopes received confirmation a week or ten days later when a high-flying formation of Canada geese crossed overhead going north. The big geese seldom err, it's almost as if they are privy to inside information.

It's now mid-March. Most of the snow is gone except on the northern slopes. Tulips and crocuses are breaking through in a protected flower bed near the house. Little buds are forming on the lilac bushes. It will be an early spring this year. Nature does't make many mistakes, nor does she follow the calendar. The creatures of nature simply anticipate future weather conditions and act accordingly. Something mysterious is going on.

How does nature know the things that not even the most sophisticated computer system can predict? How did the robins know it was safe to return? After all, they had to leave their winter feeding grounds weeks ahead of their arrival in northwestern Montana. So did the honkers. How do they know?

There's also other mysteries: like, how do animals find their way home across a long distance they have never before travelled? How do animals anticipate violent storms, avalanches, and earthquakes hours or even days before they occur? How do salmon, after spending their entire adult life at sea, find a spawning bed in the same stream where they themselves hatched? How can a flock of hundreds of black birds, and many other species, make sharp maneuvers in flight and turn in tight formation without ever having a mid-air collision? Fish swimming in schools do the same thing, changing course in unison, each seeming to know simultaneously when and in what direction to turn. How do they know? How do they communicate? It's as if a thought, or movement, generates a field of information—an aura of intelligence which instantly transmits an intention and a command.

These and other questions have long plagued the

mind of naturalists and biologists. Despite consider-able research in recent times, we know very little about animal navigation. Practically nothing definitive can be said concerning their uncanny ability to communicate, sometimes over distances which preclude any possibility of sensual coordination. Concerning their ability to anticipate future weather patterns and natural events, well... For now I'll leave you hanging on a mystery, but I promise to return with a bag full of metaphors and hypotheses concerning navigation, covert communication, and precognition.

Navigation

You'd think we ought to be able to determine how ants, bees, pigeons, fish, and other creatures find their way through the wilds. We have time-lapse photography, compact monitoring devices, hundreds of scientific measuring instruments, and thousands of curious observers taking field notes. From this research comes many theories. Some credit Sun or Moon as navigational reference points. Others rely upon an internal interpretation of polarized light, most incorporate Earth's magnetic field in some unexplained manner, all involve extraordinary sensual capabilities. In the end all fail to explain the mechanics by which an animal can determine its present location in relation to its intended destination.[1]

For instance, current research suggests that salmon, steelhead trout, and other migratory fish have an incredible sense of smell which directs them to their spawning grounds. Each stream supposedly has a unique scent due to minerals and foliage which become dissolved in, or absorbed by, the water as it flows its course. This smell registers in memory and thus guides the spawners back to their ancestral home. Even though some research results tend to validate the scent theory, they skilfully skip over pertinent details. My personal skepticism is: how, if located somewhere in the middle of the Pacific Ocean, can a salmon smell the mouth of the Columbia River from a distance of a thousand or more miles? The Columbia is a big river but its water certainly loses its unique characteristics shortly after discharge into the sea. Is it reasonable to think that a scent gradient spreads throughout the Pacific? I doubt it.

Perhaps we could say that come spawning time each fish naturally drifts east until encountering land (the North American Continent), then cruises north and south until it encounters the proper scent. The hitch in this idea is: how do fish know which way is east? Sure, the daily rising of the Sun tells us humans which way is east, so does a compass if we have one handy. Do fish have reasoning power which allows them to deduce that Sun always rises in the east, or do they have a built-in compass? Perhaps they have both, or simply a thing called instinct which unerringly determines the cardinal directions. Even so, other problems come to mind. The scent hypothesis assumes stable conditions in the environment; that is, it requires that nothing happens while the fish is at sea for three or four years to alter the scent of its home grounds. Clear-cut logging, mining, the discharge of waste into freshwater streams, a host of natural events such as mud slides, volcanic eruptions, and drouth could drastically change the scent of water by eliminating some ingredients while adding alien substances.

The scent theory is simple, it answers a question, but many perplexities remain. Whatever the process, salmon possess abilities beyond our comprehension.

Why not just say they benefit from an obscure intelligence? More specifically, they interact with a silent messenger which has knowledge beyond our understanding.

The infallible navigational ability of migratory spawners is indeed incredible, but they are merely retracing a route previously traveled. Maybe they have a remarkable memory, a mental map which shows every twist and turn in a river and stream. But memory alone fails to explain the homing instinct.

Consider cases where an animal finds its way home without having previously made the journey under its own locomotion. Michael Long (refer to superscript 1 above) describes a 1957 experiment during which 18 Laysan albatrosses on Midway atoll in the Pacific were banded and transported by aircraft to Japan, the Philippines, the Mariana, Marshall, and Hawaiian Islands, and the state of Washington. Upon release, 14 of the 18 birds found their way back to Midway. One averaged 317 miles per day. Quoting Long, "leading researchers...conclude that, existing theories of bird navigation do not fully explain their homing behavior."

We sometimes think that domestic animals have surrendered their instincts as a result of their close association with man. That is, domestication dulls their ability to fend for themselves. My experience doesn't support this idea. A good horse will bring you home regardless of how hopelessly lost you become while riding or hunting in the mountains, and it's usually the shortest way, not merely back-tracking.

Cats and dogs are smarter than we generally give them credit. They quickly catch onto our habits thus enabling them to anticipate our actions, particularly so when it involves them in some way—feeding, being left alone, etc. Then at other times they seem able to read our minds from a distance: like waiting at the door several minutes before our actual arrival, or aberrant behavior when something unpleasant happens to their master while he or she is away from home. And they too are territorial, defensive of their space whether it be invaded by an unfamiliar human or another animal. They know it's their home, and they always know the way back if perchance they become separated.

Every year we read or hear accounts where cats and dogs, who while traveling, become separated from their owner and then find their way back home. The following is an uncanny example: In 1922, a dog named Hector became separated from his master in Vancouver, British Columbia. Come departure time, and unable to find his dog, the man boarded his ship and left port without Hector. Hector, unable to find his master, roamed the dock and then stowed away on a docked ship bound for Tokyo. Upon arrival Hector found his master's anchored ship. Hector could have boarded any of five ships that day in Vancouver, but he chose the only one scheduled for Japan. What's more remarkable, Hector's master didn't live in Tokyo, he was first officer on a Dutch ship.[2] Who, or what, guided Hector on his voyage?, a silent messenger?

Animal navigational methods are indeed complex. Though research suggests several possible theories, the actual mechanics remain a mystery.

Communication

Even more baffling are nature's method of communication. By this, I mean the transmission and reception of information to and from remote locations. This phenomenon not only serves biological systems, it also applies to inanimate matter.

Inanimate Matter

An interesting example of inanimate matter keeping in touch involves certain chemical reactions. Most chemical reactions proceed quickly to static conditions (equilibrium). A solution of sulfuric acid is an example of equilibrium condition. A bottle of such acid can sit on a shelf indefinitely without changing. Individual molecules wander at random in the bottle completely oblivious of one another. They bounce off one another and the wall of the bottle in a continuous state of turmoil. However, a form of self-organization occurs when certain compounds are prevented from reaching equilibrium. This is achieved by introducing energy or additional matter which establishes and maintains the non-steady state condition. The molecules, when receiving energy or matter from an external source, begin to react in an ordered way. Thus, randomness yields to structure.

Coveney and Highfield, in their book *The Arrow of Time*,[3] describe several examples, one which uses a thin film of silicone oil compressed between two glass plates. At room temperature (equilibrium) the molecules are in random motion looking as expected, like any other thin film of oil. But after applying heat to the bottom plate, an intricate hexagonal pattern emerges. The pattern holds for as long as heat enters the system (the system held far-from-equilibrium). Then after removing the heat source, the pattern disappears as random motion again dominates the system. It's as if all the molecules received simultaneous instructions to organize, including specifications concerning the pattern they were to take. Quoting Coveney and Highfield, "The distance over which this hexagonal pattern forms is 100 million times greater than the distance between individual molecules." How, other than an inherent urge to self-organize, do they know what to do? Some information field exists, a silent intelligence (mute to us) which transmits a command and a blueprint.

Less apparent energies can and do directly influence physical systems. Human intelligence consistently disturbs experiments in the study of quantum mechanics. For example, a physicist may wish to observe what happens when a highly energized particle collides with another particle. The experimenter knows in advance that two possibilities exist: he or she will see either a shattering of particles or wave forms of energy. If the experimenter designs the apparatus to observe a wave form, that is what's observed. If, however, he or she designs the apparatus to detect particles, a shattering of particles occur. The intellect (an obscure energy source) of the observer determines the outcome.

Somehow, human intellect effects physical matter and/or energy. This paradox leads most scientists to the conclusion that quantum theory casts considerable doubt upon our conventional view of reality. To laymen like us, it appears that accelerated particles are quite obliging; they strive to appease physicists playing with multimillion dollar toys. Nonetheless, nature has a subtle way of informing matter, both animate and inanimate, concerning what is happening or will happen at remote locations. Is this another example of silent messengers; a confirmation of mind over matter?

Probabilities and uncertainty are unavoidable characteristics of quantum theory; non-equilibrium chemical reactions produce some strange results. Both react to unknown, or unidentified, information fields. Lacking an explanatory theory, we will assume that silent messengers lurk in the background.*

Biological Systems

Physical systems are complex; some aspects of biological systems are elusive, often intruding into the metaphysical. When studying physical systems, physicists and chemists can usually call upon mathematics to describe and predict the unusual. Nobody has yet derived a series of mathematical equations to describe what happens at the cellular level in biological systems, to say nothing of explaining an entire organism. The following is a very simple experiment which defies common sense and scientific explanation.

> "On a recent winter night, John and Lisa were making love in their San Diego hotel room. About five miles away in a downtown laboratory, a strip chart recorder was registering wild fluctuations that measured changes in the electrical activity of a solution of some of Lisa's white blood cells from saliva which she had donated a few hours earlier.
> "The moment the lovemaking stopped, fluctuations in the electrical current ceased. After a few hours' sleep (and a quiet chart), the activity abruptly started up when a morning lovemaking session began. And just as sharply they both died down together several minutes later."

This quote is the opening two paragraphs of Brian O'Leary's book, *Exploring Inner and Outer Space.*[4] A first impression might lead us to conclude that O'Leary is more qualified to discuss outer space because he was a NASA scientist/astronaut during the Apollo program,

---

*It's quite possible that physicists will identify and quantify any number of new energy fields during the next few decades, thus explaining the role of some silent messengers. Up until the mid-nineteenth century the various forces in the electromagnetic field were mystical. Now, today, a physics reference book contains numerous equations applicable to these fields.

then deputy team leader of the Mariner 10 Venus-Mercury television science team. But first impressions can be misleading. He has since left NASA and is now one of a growing number of scientists who question the methodology of present day science.

O'Leary is not a renegade scientist gone berserk; he has served on the science faculty of three leading universities since leaving NASA. He has written and lectured extensively in his area of expertise. Fortunately, to the benefit of mankind, his interest turned toward the paranormal. The above quote is an example of the paranormal, a mystery, something which science can't explain. With regard to that experiment, he concludes, "This one experiment proved to me as a skeptical scientist that we could measure force fields of communications in consciousness that defy the known laws of physics." Those force fields constitute what I call silent messengers.

Force fields, silent messengers, by whatever name, similar phenomena may also fit into what British biochemist Rupert Sheldrake terms morphic fields. Sheldrake has also left the mainstream of conventional science to explore in virgin territory. His book, *The Presence of the Past,*[5] is an elaborate and excellently researched argument supporting his hypothesis of *formative causation.* Now, this isn't a very *informative* name for any idea. What does it mean?

It is Sheldrake's version of what other biologists term morphogenesis: the study of the evolution of form in plants and animals, form referring to physical structure and appearance. Few of us have become wildly excited about this branch of biology—I can't remember the last time *Good Morning America* featured such a discussion. Nonetheless, it is a valid consideration of science because it is basic to any study of biological evolution.

Sheldrake's hypothesis minimizes genetic inheritance as the prime causative factor which determines body shape, general characteristics, and individual behavior. That is, genetics alone do not dictate whether an embryo develops into a cow rather than becoming a horse or pig or whatever. He therefore has assumed the role of a rebel biochemist since conventional thinking affirms that genetics control body form, behavior and social organization to some extent, and general species characteristics. He is doing to biology what Brian O'Leary is doing to physics: showing that traditional science suffers an inadequacy.

Sheldrake begins by showing that in early stages of development the embryo of a fish, a tortoise, a chick, a rabbit, and a man are strikingly similar. For example, they all have a gill slit between the eye and forelimb. But this gill slit disappears in later stages of development in all species except the fish. Rather than being exclusively controlled by genetics, Sheldrake's hypothesis proposes that form and character come from instructions contained in a field of information pertinent to each individual species. He terms this information source *morphic fields* (morphic from the Greek meaning *form*).

Morphic fields are better understood as the habits of nature (he describes his reasoning in detail). That is, each species has a history of developed habits to which subsequent individuals adhere. Their biological form, their social organization, and unique traits produce these habits, after which the habits determine the general characteristics and behavior of subsequent members of the species. Morphic resonance provides the method of communication.

So, what is morphic resonance? Here's Sheldrake's definition, coming from the glossary of his book:

> *morphic resonance*: The influence of previous structures of activity on subsequent similar structures of activity organized by morphic fields. Through morphic resonance, formative causal influences pass through or across both space and time, and these influences are assumed not to fall off with distance in space or time, but they come only from the past. The greater the degree of similarity, the greater the influence of morphic resonance. In general, morphic units [loosely meaning an individual of a species] closely resemble themselves in the past and are subject to self-resonance from their own past states."

Far-fetched?

I think not. If nature could guide Hector, the dog, several thousand miles across the Pacific to there find his master's ship docked in a foreign port, where do we set the upper limits of her ability? Morphic resonance provides a possible explanation for many of the mysteries of nature. For instance, what caused the excitation of Lisa's white cells in a laboratory five miles away while she herself was making love?* Rupert Sheldrake might like the opportunity to answer that question. His morphic resonance may be another component of O'Leary's force fields. Silent messengers may be an agency for both.

The metaphor of silent messengers is a convenient way to express the apparent communication network which serves nature. Admittedly, it's a rather carefree concept which doesn't begin to describe how the system works: but neither do force fields or morphic resonance (yet). My terminology assumes that information abides

---

*Such phenomena are not unusual—quantum effects for example. Sometimes termed nonlocality, any number of scientists are investigating the correspondence between events separated by space.

out there somewhere and that a message is sent to an agency. That agency, whether it be an individual, a species, or a planetary ecosystem, receives knowledge and incorporates it into the agency's activities. But from where or what source do silent messengers pick up their information?

Memories in Time

To answer the above question, we must mentally invent some sort of universal data bank (UDB). (What did writers use for analogy before desktop computers invaded homes and offices)? This data bank, unlike a computer, has immeasurable storage capacity and its speed of transmission is instantaneous—not restricted to the speed of light as in electrical circuits. It contains an enormous volume of data to which silent messengers have instant access. Every atom, every particle in the Universe, is a terminal which means that silent messengers can disseminate information to the smallest molecule anywhere, anytime. Perhaps Sheldrake's morphic fields could be a component of this data bank; O'Leary's force fields might occupy another niche.

The universal data bank is ever evolving and expanding. It receives a continuous influx of new knowledge and ideas regardless of where they originate. And as soon as received, each piece of information becomes immediately accessible to silent messengers. Each fragment of knowledge, regardless of its content or source of origin, propagates instantly throughout the Universe in energetic wave form. These waves have an infinite number of frequency and amplitude combinations. But where does all this information originate?

As inferred, the UDB becomes a memory bank, a record of every thought and event since the beginning of time. A thought is an energy form, as is an idea, a concept, the history of an event. When something happens, or a thought emerges from consciousness, its energy immediately registers in the UDB. Again using computer jargon, the registered input enters the public domain. It is immediately available to silent messengers, thus within reach of anyone, anytime. This concept somewhat nullifies the legal implications of plagiarism because very few ideas are truly original. Silent messengers deliver ideas which may seem new and fresh to the recipient but which in fact may be very old.

We frequently encounter situations where strangers separated by distance receive similar ideas almost concurrently. For instance, Isaac Newton is regarded as the inventor of calculus, but German philosopher Gottfried Leibniz independently discovered this important branch of mathematics before Newton published his works. This isn't an isolated instance, a history of the evolution of knowledge is replete with such examples, of cases where two or more total strangers independently receive similar insights near simultaneously.

Many of us, when reading or attending a lecture bearing on a topic of interest, occasionally think, "Wow, I was thinking the same thing not long ago." Another example: the first draft of this chapter was complete before I ever read Sheldrake's, *The Presence of the Past*. Needless to say, I became excited about his ideas because they paralleled my thoughts. His work was technical, thoroughly researched, well presented. Mine is general, mostly metaphorical or analogous, a synthesis of many diverse thoughts from various disciplines and mythology. I take many liberties with science and natural history to form my opinions; so, recognizing the apparent relevance, I felt compelled to rewrite this chapter to include Sheldrake's work because his ideas support my theme better than anything I could write or say. Perhaps I was the fortunate recipient of mental morphic resonance emanating from Rupert Sheldrake.

Precognition

Force fields, morphic fields, a universal data bank, or whatever, none have predictive power. They apply only to the past and/or present. In the case of morphic fields, the past shapes the present. In O'Leary's experiment, force fields are an energy which directly causes an interaction between two events separated by space. The UDB contains information relevant to both the past and present but is ignorant concerning the future. Coupled with silent messengers, the attributes of these various fields provide a possible explanation for animal navigational systems and a means of communication for physical matter. However, none of these ideas account for precognition, the knowing in advance of a future event.

Can nature foretell the future?

If not, how did the robins and geese know it was time to go north? Or consider this account, quoted from Francis Hitching, *The Mysterious World*, (note: 2 in the Appendix):

> "In February, 1939, St Bernard dogs in the Swiss Alps refused, for the first time ever, to go for their morning walk with the monks. An hour later an avalanche engulfed the part of the track that they would have been on in normal circumstances."

Will researchers next tell us that animals, in addition to having a built-in magnetic compass, a sensitive apparatus to detect scent gradients, an extraordinary sensual perception, they also have a barometer and seismograph fused within their brain? It's a common knowledge out here in rural settings that nature is more reliable in weather prediction than the morning newscast. Elk and deer are predominantly nocturnal, that is, they much prefer to feed at night. However, if they perceive an immanent storm, they leave the timber to feed in daylight. Therefore, if they leave their bed at mid-day to start feeding, it's time to call the children home because a blizzard is brewing. Moreover, the old-timers say that deer and elk regulate the fall breeding season to capitalize on optimum weather conditions when it comes time to drop their young the next spring. I'm not aware of any scientific studies which verify this observation, but approaching old-timerhood myself, it fits with my unrecorded recollections. Nature just seems to know what is in store for tomorrow.

The squirrels who scamper through the fir trees around our house give an early indication of what to expect during the coming winter. If they spend the summer chattering to one another from the tree tops, not to worry because winter will be relatively open and mild. But if they start storing tree cones in July or August, look out because we have a long bitter winter ahead. Nature cares for its creatures, silent messengers deliver information essential to survival.

Human prediction is old, old stuff. It probably goes back to the first story tellers. An ancient shaman wasn't worthy of esteem if she or he couldn't foretell coming events or circumstances effecting the tribe or community. Then, having foretold the future, the tribe expected her or him to circumvent the event, or at least to mitigate the consequences.

Shamanism carried forward from hunter/gatherer societies to the early agricultural communities in

Mesopotamia. In time shamanism yielded to an ever growing priesthood which assumed the spiritual duties of mankind. Eventually an elite priesthood became primarily concerned with mundane affairs thus neglecting spiritual duties. Dissidents, appalled by the apathy of the temple, foretold drastic events if mankind didn't change his ways and conform to certain rules and ideas. The Hebrew Prophets became vehement advocates for reform during the first millenium, BC. The Old Testament of the Bible is, among other things, a respectable compilation of ancient fortune-telling.

This isn't intended to belittle shamans or the Hebrew Prophets. I bring the matter up to show that silent messengers were active far back in history. Some predictions made by ancient prophets and modern psychics have proven quite accurate. Some are way off base. Inaccuracy can result from: silent messages not being properly interpreted, it represents wishful thinking on the part of the prophet, the prophet fabricates a story to bring personal gain, prophesies are deliberate misrepresentations intended to control and manipulate others. It is enough to acknowledge the existence of false prophets; for our purpose, we will concentrate on silent messages which convey truth or perceived reality.

Fortune telling is now generally considered entertainment at best, at worst a hoax. We immediately envision a gaudy Gypsy lady hunched over a cup of tea leaves making dire predictions or foretelling a romantic adventure. Gypsies have pretty well disappeared from county fairs and gone back to wherever they came from. Nonetheless, considerable skepticism remains concerning any form of fortune telling. This is unfortunate because it prompts us to ignore valid insights delivered by silent messengers (distrusting intuition, discussed in a later chapter).

So, how do we explain accurate predictions? Can nature remember the future? Fred Alan Wolf thinks so.

Here we meet another physicist who recognizes the inadequacy of modern scientific methodology to explain the Universe in which we find ourselves. Wolf's book, *Parallel Universes*,[6] proposes an infinite number of coexisting universes. Some of these universes exist in the past, some in the present, others in the future. He describes an intricate scenario explaining how awareness, or consciousness, flirts with the past and future as well as abiding in the present.

We acknowledge that the past can influence the present, the present effect the future. This isn't a difficult concept. But to think that the future can alter the past and present is beyond our conceptual ability. We say that the past is immutable; the future is yet to happen. The present is the only reality worth considering (we are back to the argument concerning the Arrow of Time, Chapter Three).

If Fred Wolf's parallel universes do actually exist, we don't need silent messengers. Nature can remember the future. Therefore, if I could remember an auto accident in which I become injured next year, I wouldn't take the trip when that day rolls around. In this case, the future never happens.

We can't categorically state that Wolf's parallel universes don't exist. But the idea exceeds my sense of reason by several orders of magnitude. Besides, I think we can find a simpler explanation for how nature foretells the future.

Let's first think about some modern day prophets—scientists. They consume considerable time and expense offering hypotheses foretelling the future: for instance, predicting the ultimate fate of the Universe.

But it's still a clouded issue because silent messengers have withheld critical data, the missing mass for one thing. A few garbled messages concerning dark matter and superstrings have come through. But the information is fuzzy, lacking detail and a means of verification.

If we reduce the scale, say to the size of the solar system, physicists are confident that the Sun will burn out in five billion years, plus or minus a few hundred million years. This is a safe prediction because who of us will be here to offer criticism if it doesn't happen on schedule? Time is an ally because it provides insulation against such criticism. Scientific prophesy is a noble endeavor, it keeps a lot of Ph.D.'s employed, research institutes receive huge grants (usually coming from the taxpayer's pocket), and it's not particularly risky, especially in situations where verification is impossible.

But prediction becomes more complex if we reduce the scale to earthly proportions. The shroud of time doesn't shield geologists and seismologists from criticism when they fail to pinpoint the day and hour of volcanic eruptions and earthquakes. They can scrutinize seismic strip charts, map fault planes, know what causes an earthquake, but when it comes to the final verdict they can only speak in terms of statistical probabilities. Climatologists know the mechanics which cause an avalanche, they can recognize potentially dangerous conditions and issue warnings, but again they are dealing with probabilities, not certainties. Consider also the plight of the poor meteorologist. They have sophisticated data gathering systems, high-powered computers with which to process the data, and they understand the dynamics which bring storm clouds together. Need I comment on the reliability of weather forecasts?

How do silent messengers know those things which technology can't predict with any degree of certainty?— because they have access to the universal data bank? Scientists must deduce data from a mere sampling of information: an averaging process involving projection, interpolation, and downright speculation using theories which may or may not be correct. If, however, science had sound theories and minute to minute knowledge of conditions prevailing at all terminals (every atom), it might then produce reliable predictions. But alas, we aren't likely to have this technical ability for some time to come. Silent messengers have that ability. They monitor every atom in the Universe. They know what is going on everywhere, all the time.

Man-made weather predictions are particularly difficult because atmospheric conditions are dynamic, changing from minute to minute. We have all noticed how fast clouds can move across the sky, how a cloud image resembling a fish soon changes to look like the head of a dog, or something else. It's apparent that atmospheric conditions are never stable, or predictable. Now suppose that we wished to make a dedicated effort toward achieving 99% accuracy in weather prediction. To get a more representative sampling of data, we set up an elaborate monitoring system to collect data from every cubic mile of atmosphere covering Mother Earth. The system would record the direction and velocity of upper air currents, humidity, barometric pressure, temperature, all the variables needed to calculate future weather patterns. This data would feed into a super-computer programmed with equations to evaluate the weather over every square mile of Earth's surface. Could we expect 99% accuracy for a week in advance?

Maybe. But by the time the computers had crunched

all the numbers we may need to search last week's weather reports to determine the accuracy of the system. Aside from the prodigious expense in setting up the system, it's not a very practical idea.

Now let's consider the problems associated with earthquake prediction? Suppose that we locate sensitive stress detection devices at one foot intervals up and down and lengthwise of the plane of the San Andreas fault. Then a minute by minute recording of the various stresses feed into a computer located in Los Angeles for analysis. Presuming the proper programming, could the computer issue a warning in time to evacuate the city? Probably not. The computer might lay under a pile of rubble before the computation is complete.

Time and insufficient data are the enemies of Earth bound prediction methods. But this isn't the case for silent messengers. They have instant knowledge of all things through all time. They can and do anticipate future weather patterns and geologic events. How far into the future can they see? Maybe a year or more for some situations, maybe much longer for others. Since the present influences the future and human will (our actions or lack of action) shapes the present, they must continually revise their analysis to account for our unwise activities. Troublesome perhaps, but we can assume that they are able to issue a timely warning concerning most matters for those who are listening.

And just who is it that listens?

Robins and geese apparently have good ears. So do St Bernard dogs. Apparently some people also listen because they have been heard to say, "a storm is coming, I know because I can feel it in my bones," (my bones sometimes complain but I suspect it is age related rather than weather).

The predictive power of silent messengers involves

more than recalling history and the maintenance of knowledge concerning present conditions. It implies something else at work. But what?

Predetermined, Or Evolutionary?

We might think that the future is a hard indelible fact, predetermined at the start of time. The growth and final destiny of the Universe will proceed according to a plan as decreed by the Creator. If that plan is to change, it is by will of the Creator and has nothing to do with our daily activities. We take what's given and that's final.

Despite the many quotes allegedly emanating from the Creator as espoused by television evangelists, we're still left to wonder whether He/She routinely intervenes in the daily affairs of nature. You might be quick to say yes by pointing out the indisputable power of prayer and meditation. Beyond question, an appeal to the Creator can bring comfort, peace, a remission of pain and destitution. But do these results accrue from divine intervention, or are they an opening up of consciousness to receive a power which surrounds us every minute of life? My answer is: the power of Spirit, or the compassion of the Creator, is always present and ever accessible to those who open their consciousness. Prayer and meditation are proven techniques for receiving divine bliss and comfort, a tapping into a field of infinite love.

It seems doubtful that the Creator provides insurance against calamity or invokes special privileges for a few while neglecting the many. While it's true that certain laws of nature appear immutable, all have considerable built-in flexibility. Take gravity for instance. It is certain that if I hold a sledge hammer up high and release my grip, it will fall. It's not at all certain whether it will hit the ground or my foot. Where it lands depends upon my action or lack of action prior to letting it fall. If I held it out at arm's length, it would probably hit the ground sparing my foot. I can obviously effect the future. If I were so stupid as to stick my foot forward, I wouldn't expect my Creator to deflect the trajectory of the falling hammer so as to miss my foot. The force of gravity holds true but consequences accrue from unwise decisions. I don't expect the Creator to insulate me from my own indiscretions.

The Universe operates within a framework of laws which prescribe what happens as a consequence of certain events. And events are happenings in the present. They can occur, or be circumvented by willful intention. We have already seen that the past influences the present (morphic resonance). We now see that the present can effect the future via the power of intelligence.

Silent messengers not only convey knowledge, they can decipher and interpret information. They make judgements as to future conditions based upon past and present experience. Their inherent intelligence gives them power surpassing our wildest imagination. But they do not attempt to control the will of man (except through intuition), we come into the physical with the right of choice. Silent messengers evaluate these various choices and are thus able to foresee some future consequences.

As we have just demonstrated, silent messengers do not have a book describing the future because the future is dependent upon the events of today and yesterday. The future will write its own history. Silent messengers therefore must constantly monitor and analyze incoming data in order to predict a probable event for tomorrow, next week, or next year. They are able to compute the information received from the universal data bank in an instant. They can answer a question as soon as asked, they can solve a problem as soon as defined. But like earth-bound predictions, the farther out in time they go, inaccuracy creeps in due to the unfolding of unexpected events. Probabilities, not mandates, rule the Universe.

If silent messengers are so smart, can they foretell the ultimate fate of the Universe?

Probably not. The future is indeterminate that far out in time. The flatness problem, discussed in Chapter One, may indicate an issue yet undecided. Perhaps this is the first universe the Creator has attempted, in which case He/She is waiting to decide whether to repeat the cycle. We can't possibly know the Creator's ambitions, creating universes may be a side-line interest and we are lucky to be included in the experiment.

A Fifth Force, or Transcendent Dimensions?

The universal data bank, silent messengers, O'Leary's force fields, Sheldrake's fields, all are contrary to the known laws of physics. (They can't be quantified, identified, or expressed in equation form). Moreover, the instantaneous transmission of information throughout the Universe via physical energy fields is impossible (conventional wave forms cannot exceed the speed of light). If these fields are more than a metaphor (and they are), in what media do they propagate?

We must now think in terms of transcendent dimensions, of realms of reality beyond the physical restrictions imposed upon spacetime. A fifth dimension? Some, to explain the paranormal, have proposed the existence of a Fifth Force; that is, the existence of an undiscovered force which complements the other four known forces of physics. Perhaps I'm stumbling over semantics, but I conceive a force different from an energy field. A force (to me) implies the transmission of some form of kinetic energy (okay for O'Leary's experiment); a field implies latent or potential energy; that is, an energy which lays quiescent until requested to perform a service after which it exerts a force. Regardless, we need a transcendent dimension to liberate these elusive forces and fields from spacetime.

Beyond doubt, we are dealing with an energy form, albeit a foreign form of energy. The generation of a single thought or idea drains a small amount of physical energy from our metabolic system. The process which I then envision is that when that thought or idea escapes from consciousness, its energy converts into transcendental energy. It immediately enters the universal data bank. It becomes a fragment of human knowledge always accessible to those who tune into the proper frequency.

Lacking a better term, I call the additional dimension(s) the Realm of Spirit, the energies contained therein spiritual energies. This is the only province I can think of which is transcendental, eternal, completely immune to the restrictions imposed upon spacetime. Besides, the idea fits nicely with the theme of this book. O'Leary and Sheldrake may object to including their forces and fields within this category, but that's okay because one or both of them may discover and quantify these elusive energies.

The consignment of invisible and unknown energy fields to Spirit perhaps relegates spirutualism to the mundane, depriving it of divine attributes. But, what is divinity? Consider the possibility that Divinity itself is also evolving, forever growing, always ascending to higher levels of Being. If there is a purpose for the Universe and a higher meaning to life, perhaps both serve the intent and needs of the Creator. From our perspective the Creator is infinitely wise and compassionate, from the Creator's viewpoint, He/She may also be reaching for higher realms of consciousness.

Chapter Five

CONVERGENT CONCEPTS

Theoretical Physics and American Indian Spirituality

So far we have been through cosmology, geology, biology, general relativity, you name it. You might be wondering what any of these have to do with black holes and tepee rings. Don't lay the book aside; we are now going to get into the subject matter of the title.

First, let me remind you that before the seventeenth century nature was thought ruled by the will of the Creator. The moon rose by divine decree, as did the Sun. Day followed day, month followed month, the years flowed together from birth to death. Prayer and ceremony assured the orderly succession of seasons and lifetimes.

But Isaac Newton changed all that. His work revealed a deterministic Universe which operated with the precision of a watch. The motion of moons and planets was immutable, their movements predictable years and centuries into the future. His view was a stable ever enduring cosmos. Mathematics, not divine decree, described the mechanics of the Universe.*

---

*Newton was by no means an atheist. He was an eccentric, and often cantankerous, man who devoted much of his later life to theological issues. Like Einstein, his greatest contributions to science came early in life.

Albert Einstein brought that view into question when he published his theory of general relativity. His universe was relativistic rather than deterministic, meaning that reality itself came into question. Nothing is fixed, all information is relative to the speed, location, mass, and motion of other things. We've seen that a stationary observer will measure the passage of time different from one who is moving. But nothing is stationary. All galaxies are receding away from one another and our platform here on Earth is certainly not stationary. We exist way out in the arm of a spiral galaxy which is rotating in space. Then Earth circles Sun once a year, and compounding this motion, Earth makes a complete revolution every 24 hours. It's small wonder that we aren't dizzier than we are considering all the spinning we undergo.

Since everything and everybody are always in motion, we must have a reference point—relative to what? For instance, if I assume my desk and chair to be a stationary reference point, the airplane I hear going overhead is moving faster than I. But if I assume that the Sun is our mutual reference point, and if the plane is flying west, it is I who is moving faster (the pilot is flying into Earth's rotation thus reducing his speed by the rate at which the plane moves). If the pilot turns north or south, we both have approximately the same velocity relative to the Sun. However, if he or she turns back east, the plane and its passengers will then be moving faster than I (Earth's rotational speed plus that of the plane). Whichever, our sense of reality will always say that the plane is traveling faster because Mother Earth, not Father Sun, is our usual reference point. Einstein's theory of relativity seldom fits perceived reality.

We might think that Einstein's Universe is quite

modernistic: a brand new viewpoint concerning nature and how things work. But I venture to guess that relativity might lead us back to primal thinking, that we might see a convergence of concepts—old ideas marching alongside new theories. We might even discover that reality is relative to our training in early life, to our ingrained beliefs, to our personal view of nature. It's this personal view of nature which appears headed back toward old concepts.

This chapter purports to show the mythological similarity between modern thinking and the views of a vanquished culture which once lived close to nature. We'll first review the modern view, then look at an older view.

The New View

Let's start by recalling that Einstein's equations of general relativity are the mathematical tools used to model Big Bang theory. A number of technical problems plagued the early work; not the least troublesome was the appearance of singularities. Even physicists had an aversion to a point having infinite density. However, despite the conceptual difficulty, the idea caught on slowly and began to gain acceptance in the 1940s. But then came the Steady State hypothesis advanced by Gold, Hoyle, and Bondi and scientific opinions divided. As noted in Chapter One, the Steady State model fell from favor in the early 1960s leaving the incomplete Big Bang model.

General relativity also suggested the possibility of small isolated singularities scattered throughout the Universe. Being conjectural, the hypothesis conceived them as having a very strong gravitational field, so strong that not even a photon (a particle of light) could escape capture if it came within a certain proximity. This of course would mean that they are invisible to telescopes which receive light from outer space. These postulated anomalies in space became known as *black holes.*

Cosmology slipped into a relative state of stagnation for a few years. The possible existence of black holes became a fertile field for writers of science fiction, but some physicists remained reluctant to embrace the idea. Then British mathematician Roger Penrose solved the black hole singularity problem by applying an unusual mathematical technique to the equations of general relativity. By considering super massive stars, larger than those required to produce a neutron star, Penrose mathematically defined the conditions necessary to produce a black hole. Goodbye common sense, hello to a flood of new ideas.

Two years earlier, a young graduate student was searching for a thesis to complete his Ph.D. Unfortunately, his future appeared grim indeed because he had just been diagnosed as having ALS (Lou Gehrig disease). Why worry about your future when the history of the disease would indicate one had only a short time to live? But two years passed, and in his words, "things were going rather well for me and I had gotten engaged to a very nice girl,...but to get married, I needed a job, and in order to get a job, I needed a Ph.D."[1]

Now, more than a quarter-century later, unable to speak and confined to a wheelchair, many credit Stephen Hawking as being the world's foremost theoretical physicist. It's with great effort that he can manipulate a computer keyboard. Despite his considerable affliction, he is currently Lucasian professor of mathematics at Cambridge University—a chair once occupied by Sir Isaac Newton. Whether by coincidence or significance, he was born 300 years to the day after the death of Galileo Galilei, the first astronomer to peer into the night sky with an optical telescope. Hawking, though not an astronomer, certainly follows in the tradition of Galilei who himself trod in the footsteps of Nicolaus Copernicus (the forerunner of cosmology).

Back to 1965. Hawking picked up on Penrose's work and added a new twist. Again, in his words, "I soon realized that if one reversed the direction of time in Penrose's theorem, so that the collapse became an expansion, the conditions of his theorem would still hold...", [all quotes coming from, *A Brief History of Time*]. His calculations indicated that if the Universe is expanding, which observation confirms, the Big Bang had to have come from a singularity. Mathematical technicalities existed which confined the model to an open universe. Working jointly with Penrose, the two eliminated this and other problems in 1970. This in effect lifted the major objection to the Big Bang theory. Their work initially met with some opposition but according to Hawking:

> "...in the end our work became generally accepted and nowadays nearly everyone assumes that the universe started with a big bang singularity. It is perhaps ironic that, having changed my mind, I am now trying to convince other physicists that *there was in fact no singularity at the beginning of the universe...*" [my italics].

We will return to that final statement later. But first, we need to look at the results of Hawking's next ten years work during which he extensively studied black holes. Penrose showed the conditions under which a massive star could collapse into singularity. Hawking proceeded to investigate the properties of black holes, all described in, *A Brief History of Time*. Many other physicists were also at work, but Hawking's work led to a new proposed model of the Universe which stands in opposition to the Big Bang theory. We will also examine this idea later.

Unlike the Big Crunch referred to in Chapter One which consumes the entire Universe, we might think of a black hole as a *little crunch*. We have seen that a neutron star is the remnant, or core, of a big star after gravitational collapse (a minimum of three to four solar masses). If, however, a star of say 50 solar masses collapses, the gravitational force exceeds the internal strength of neutrons and the collapse proceeds to singularity: zero-space, infinite density. And singularity represents the center of a black hole.

At singularity matter loses its physical identity but retains its gravitational effect. Gravity is therefore extremely strong at singularity but decreases outward from the center (decreasing proportional to the square of the distance). By knowing, or assuming, the amount of mass that went into a black hole, physicists can calculate the radius of the gravitational effect which will capture light. This boundary has become known as the *event horizon*, the distance away from singularity where a photon can just prevent being drawn inside the hole. If a photon or any other particle ventures across the event horizon, it soon joins singularity, crunched into oblivion. This would be an unhappy situation for future astronauts, he or she would instantly experience the little crunch—just gone forever, leaving no relics for future cosmic archaeologists to ponder.

In Chapter Three we noted that gravity effects time; that is, the stronger the force of gravity, the slower a clock will run. Because of this effect, to a distant observer time would appear to stand still at the event horizon. One could hover in a spaceship at the event horizon indefinitely while the centuries would continue to roll by on earth. One would not age or be aware of what's happening elsewhere because consciousness and all metabolic systems would slow down accordingly.* Strange ideas indeed.

The Old View

Now I will introduce you to another remarkable man. He never went to school, he couldn't have solved the simplest math problem, he never read a book during his 87 year lifetime. He couldn't even speak the English language. By modern standards (he only died five years before Einstein) he was primitive and unlearned, and to this day he is largely unknown in the annals of American history. But despite his lack of recognition and the absence of a formal education, his wisdom was on a par with the top thinkers of today. His name was Black Elk, Holy man of the Oglala Sioux.**

Black Elk was born at a small encampment somewhere along the Little Powder River (northeastern Wyoming or southeastern Montana) during the Moon of the Popping Trees (December), 1863.*** His tribal homeland extended from the Bighorn Mountains in Wyoming, to the Yellowstone River in Montana, to the Platte River in Nebraska, to the plains of South Dakota. The Lakota were a proud people, self-sufficient, and deeply devout in observance of their native religion.

---

*Atomic, hence molecular, activity is effected by gravity; it slows down as the force of gravity decreases. This is why the atomic clocks discussed in Chapter Three ran slower when circling at high altitude.
**The Oglala Sioux people were one of seven tribes comprising the Teton Sioux Nation. All spoke the Lakota language. Hereafter, the term Lakota refers to all the Sioux people.
***Discrepancies exist concerning this date. Some references give 1862, others 1864. Perhaps Black Elk himself wasn't sure of the date.

The Sioux Holy man was born into troubled times. The Wasichus (white people) were invading lands traditionally controlled by the Lakota people, slaughtering the buffalo, and violating every traditional territorial right of the Sioux Nation. The chiefs, after council, donned their warbonnets. Almost three years to the day after Black Elk's birth, the Indians engaged Captain Fetterman and 81 of his troopers near Fort Phil Kearney, Nebraska, killing all 82 of the detachment. It was a shallow victory. It would be ten years before the Indians achieved another victory, and that would be their last. During this interval, the U.S. Army continuously attacked, dispersed, and demoralized the tribes of the area. In the spring of 1876, the Indians of many camps began retreating westward toward the Bighorn Mountains. Many tribes assembled and made camp along the Little Bighorn River in Montana just north of the Wyoming border.

Under heavy pressure from Washington, DC, the Army made preparations for a long campaign during the summer of 1876. The intent was to herd the tribes onto reservations thereby eliminating the Indian problem. The ambitious, and more than slightly egotistic, commander of the Seventh Cavalry went on reconnaissance to track down and locate the hostiles. Lt. Colonel George A. Custer came upon the camp, and we all know the outcome of the Battle of the Little Bighorn on the 25th day of June, 1876.

Black Elk was thirteen years old at the time and a witness, but not participant, of the battle. Historians still debate the details of the battle, but Black Elk gives a lucid account of the day from the Indian perspective. The Indian force divided after the victory and the Lakota group in which Black Elk traveled went southwest into the Bighorn Mountains. The tribes were on the lam, so to speak, but within a short time all but a few found themselves on various reservations.

It was on the Pine Ridge Reservation, near Manderson, South Dakota, that Nebraska poet John G. Neihardt found Black Elk in the year 1930. Neihardt cultivated a friendship with the now aging Indian and obtained permission to conduct an extended interview. Working through an interpreter (Black Elk's son), Neihardt reconstructed the life story of Black Elk. In 1932, Neihardt published a book, *Black Elk Speaks*.[2]

Later, in 1947, a young scholar named Joseph Epes Brown wished to meet and interview the now ailing and nearly blind old Indian. Neihardt advised Brown that Black Elk probably wouldn't talk with him, but Brown persisted. He found Black Elk picking potatoes with his family in Nebraska, and with some trepidation, approached the group. Black Elk, solemn with the wisdom of age, reproached Brown asking why he had taken so long to get there—that he knew that he was coming and that he wished to relate and record for future generations the sacred rituals of his people.* The two men, one young, the other very old, established instant friendship and Black Elk invited Brown to stay the winter with them on the reservation. From this long collaboration came Brown's book, *The Sacred Pipe*, published in 1953,** three years after Black Elk's death.

These two books, coming from the lips of a Native American who endured perilous times, represent the earliest works describing the Plains Indian culture

---

*Black Elk worried in vain that the Lakota traditions would accompany him to the grave. In 1978, after enactment of the Native American Religious Freedom Act, numerous medicine men and women came from underground to practice their old ways openly.
**Still in print and available from the University of Oklahoma Press.

and religion available to the general public (the earlier work of pulp journalists centered around sensationalism). It's not entirely correct to speak of Indian *religious beliefs* because the Lakota language has no word equivalent to religion. Most Native American traditions don't divide life into two categories (secular and religion); they lived their beliefs rather than talking about them. Perhaps a better English interpretation might say that Indians *walked the sacred path,* or as Black Elk termed it, the red road. Everything in Indian life was sacred, including Mother Earth, all plants and animals, even the wind which came from four sacred directions. Let's just say that Black Elk related his *philosophy* and the Indian way of viewing nature. Brown, in a later book, *The Spiritual Legacy of the American Indian,* gives us a glimpse into the Native American perspective as follows:

> "...each dwelling, no matter how simple, is an image of the cosmos. Dimensions of the sacred are made specific in every situation and are intensified through an enormous variety of special rites and ceremonies which embrace each person's life and the totality of *all* life."[3]

The dimensions of the sacred are many. Central to Black Elk's philosophy was the *flowering tree* which in a mythological sense represented the tree of life, in a practical sense an actual tree was/is used during the Sundance, the most sacred of Lakota ceremonies. All things and all life revolve around the flowering tree. Participants in the Sundance circle the flowering tree, moving clockwise around the Sacred Hoop, doing their individual ritual. The Sundance is a ritual of renewal, each trip around the hoop (circle) is the natural way, the way nature manifests itself to man. He said that everything tries to be round, the Sun is round, as is the

Earth and the moon. Birds make their nest in a circle, the wind when blowing its strongest swirls, the Sun and moon make a circle through the sky each day, the changing seasons form a circle from winter to winter, even the life of man travels a circle from infancy to infancy (senility), and so with everything where power moves.

Confirming Brown's quote above concerning the shape of the simplest of dwellings, Black Elk noted that their tepees were round like the nest of birds, and these were set in a circle. Black Elk's philosophy is well summarized by the modern expression, "what goes around, comes around."

Merging the Old View With the New

What possible link connects Stephen Hawking to Black Elk? It's hard to imagine a more diverse background, a wider gap in culture, more disparity in time and circumstance. Consider the contrast: Hawking, confined to a wheelchair, holding a prestigious position, recognized internationally, laboring with equations few of us have ever seen; Black Elk, spirit as free as the prairie breeze, mounted on a fleet pony, living in a reservation hut, unknown except to his people. Their only similarity, the single link, is a convergence of concepts—Hawking's black holes, Black Elk's tepee rings.

This requires some clarification!

The connection is mystical; that is, black holes are mysterious objects hiding in space. At the event horizon time ceases to flow, at the core (singularity) matter ceases to exist. A black hole is an anomaly in space, a place separate and apart from the Universe. It would be the only place where one could escape the restraints of time and space (not recommended, however). Some physicists even speculate that a black hole is the door to a parallel universe, that matter from our universe spurts through the singularity to enter a companion universe. These are mystic ideas indeed, more mythological than concrete.

Theoretically, black holes come in three varieties. The simplest is a static hole, another is an electrically charged hole, the final and most elaborate is a spinning black hole. Let's confine our thoughts to static black holes because they are easier to describe.

Recall that anything which crosses the event horizon would rapidly gravitate toward the center and thus become a part of the singularity. Symbolically, you could visualize a static black hole as being a miniature model of a collapsing universe which ends in a big crunch. We could expect different dynamics, particularly with respect to time. A static black hole of about 25 solar masses would have an event horizon with a radius of less than 100 miles. The race toward singularity would appear almost instantaneous whereas collapse of the Universe will require billions of years. The fact remains, matter crossing the event horizon of a black hole is on a collision course leading to its initial condition. It completes a cycle: from singularity, a first cause resulting in the Big Bang, energy transforming into physical matter, matter crossing the event horizon, crunched back to singularity in a black hole.

The initial condition is the beginning, or starting point of the cycle. By definition, a cycle describes a series of events which occur sequentially during a dynamical process. The cycle ends when a system either runs out of energy or returns to the initial condition. Sometimes a system winds down like the mainspring in a watch, other systems having sufficient inherent energy may return to the initial condition and then begin another cycle.

We can have an open cycle which proceeds in a predictable manner from point A to point B. This fits the case of artificial or mechanical systems. During a mechanical cycle, we pump energy into a process expecting that it will produce a certain end product, the operation then terminates, the process is complete. We may wish to repeat the cycle to obtain another product, but the system is not self-replicating because another cycle requires the input of outside intelligence and energy (an auto assembly line for example).

The transmission of an alternating electrical current is another example of an open cycle. It's a mechanical process where a generator introduces energy into a distribution system. Things work fine while the generator continues operation, but when a bearing goes out, so do the lights. The propagation of sound waves produced by lightning is an example of an open natural system. A lightning flash is a rapid discharge of energy into the atmosphere. This produces a shock wave (sound) which propagates outward from the flash. As the sound wave travels farther from the source, its energy dissipates and the level of noise decreases until finally it becomes so weak we can't hear it.

With closed cycles, many are self-replicating in that they return to the initial condition, then repeat themselves without intellectual intervention or deliberate action such as introducing more external energy. Such systems also need energy to proceed, but it is self-contained or supplied by a natural mechanism. Gravity (a natural force) would be the energy source causing a collapse resulting in a closed Universe. Inertia (kinetic energy, or mass in motion) keeps the Earth rotating on its axis; it also supplies the energy to maintain our annual orbit around the Sun. The Sun itself furnishes the energy needed by all earthly biological systems. Either directly or indirectly, the Universe itself provides the energy required to power natural closed systems.*

The dynamics of a closed system can be shown as a circle like that of Fig. 5-1. Point A corresponds to the initial condition: a place or time when a process begins, and where specific conditions prevail within the system. As the process proceeds, it traces the circumference of the circle, moving clockwise in this case. At point B the process is at a certain stage or phase, point C is a later phase, point D still later. The process

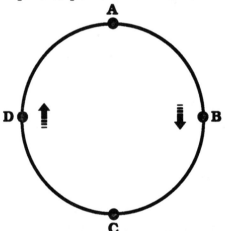

Fig. 5-1: Closed Cycle
A—The Initial Condition;
B—Intermediate Stage;
C—A More Advanced Stage;
D—Returning To The Initial Condition.

*Natural systems can run a long time on inherent energy, but eventually the energy source will dissipate. For instance, the gravitational attraction of matter upon matter robs energy from our solar system—albeit very gradual. One effect is that Earth's rotation rate declines slowly which causes the days to lengthen. Other things not considered, and given enough time, a day would stretch into 100 hours thus giving new meaning to *a long winter night.*

continues and finally comes back to point A. The cycle is complete, the original condition again prevails. If the system is self-replicating, a new cycle begins which repeats the previous cycle. The conditions at point B will always be similar to those of preceding cycles (it's always dark at midnight regardless of which day it is).

Subcycles may exist within a larger, more comprehensive cycle. For example, with a closed universe, expansion from singularity and contraction to singularity represents the ultimate closed system. However, during this time millions of subcycles are operative. A case in point: biological evolution is a closed system working within a much larger system; that is, a species comes into being and then goes extinct, its exit marked by the introduction of a new species. The appearance of modern man is a subsystem within a subsystem; one person's life span is an even smaller subsystem. The species cycle is self-repeating; on a personal level, one person's life isn't (or is it?)

The occurrence of a black hole would be a subsystem operating within the grand system. Again referring to Fig. 5-1, point A (the initial condition) would represent the singularity existing just before the Big Bang. Then came the bang and the Universe begins expanding as we move clockwise around the circle. Matter comes into being, galaxies form, stars begin to shine. Then, somehow a giant star implodes forming a black hole at point B. It gulps down any matter or light foolish enough to wander inside its event horizon. Infalling matter proceeds immediately to a singularity similar to that from which it originated; or in other words, that matter has returned to its initial condition. A subcycle is concluded.

Would the preceding scenario be a repetitive cycle? I haven't read of any physicist bold enough to suggest a mini-bang coming from the singularity of a black hole. But who knows, maybe black holes supply the material needed to support the Steady State model proposed by Hoyle, Gold, and Bondi. (I rather doubt that this idea will catch on).

How do black holes fit into the grand scheme? Again referring to Fig. 5-1, assume that point A represents the Big Bang beginning a universal cycle. At point B a black hole forms, it's just drifting around gobbling up unsuspecting prey. However, if the Universe closes, point C might represent the beginning of the universal contraction phase, at point D conditions in the Universe become increasingly chaotic. As the Universe shrinks all singularities within black holes would likely join the parade leading toward the Big Crunch. Mysterious and greedy they may be, but they can't escape getting a taste of their own medicine. (Stephen Hawking would consider such speculation a moot point because he has a proposal which supersedes Big Bang theory).

For now, however, let's see how Black Elk's philosophy fits the description of a closed repetitive cycle. Referring again to Fig. 5-1, consider point A as being the spring equinox (the Moon of the Snowblind), a time of renewal. The snow begins melting, the days become longer and warmer, the ponies shed their winter coat. Point B is the summer solstice (Moon of Making Fat), new grass arrives, the chokecherries bloom, the deer and elk and buffalo nourish the newborn and grow sleek and fat. Point C is a time to hunt, to pick wild fruit, to dry meat, to find a suitable camp near water and plenty of firewood. The winter equinox (Moon of the Popping Trees) comes at point D, this being a time of rest, introspection, purification. During the complete cycle some members of the tribe have died, to be replaced by new arrivals. A new cycle begins, new life returns.

Now let's hear what Stephen Hawking has to say, this being the premise of his book, A *Brief History of Time*.

I won't provide the details and reasoning associated with Hawking's idea because he deemed it a book length subject. I will merely give my interpretation of what Hawking has proposed as a new model of the Universe.

As noted in an earlier quote, Hawking has changed his mind concerning the possible fate of the Universe. It is indeed ironic, that after spending the large part of two decades studying singularities and black holes, he now says there is no need for a singularity or even the Big Bang. His proposed model, if eventually proven correct, would negate the search for the missing mass. It might stimulate additional ideas which lead to Einstein's lifelong ambition of finding a theory for everything (Grand Unified Theory). Though Hawking doesn't say so in direct terms, his proposed no boundary model is the ultimate closed repetitive cycle (he has little if anything to say about any type of cycle).

Hawking's no boundary model states that the Universe is finite but without an edge or any discernible boundary (try finding the edge of a sphere). It was, is, and always will be, without beginning and without end. It does allow expansion and contraction, but not to singularity where the laws of physics break down. His model is somewhat like Black Elk's circles—you can neither find the beginning nor the end of its circumference.

Now I will superimpose my interpretation of Hawking's proposed no boundary model on Fig. 5-1. At point A the Universe is quite small, extremely dense, hot beyond imagination, beginning a new expansion. As the expansion continues temperatures drop, nebulas form, galaxies and stars come into being. At point B (not necessarily one-fourth way around the circumference) thermonuclear reactions ignite in the core of stars, supernovas blast elemental particles into interstellar space, solar systems form. Between points B and C billions of life forms evolve throughout the Universe, stars burn out, the average temperature declines. Between points C and D species begin going into extinction, only a few galaxies are left shining, the contraction phase is in progress. From point D back to the initial condition the average temperature climbs, density increases, all life has perished, chaos reigns (no, time doesn't run backward). The Creator takes a holiday to welcome back His/Her returning creatures (my idea, not Hawking's). Back to point A, a new cycle begins.

Myth and Theory

So, what's the connection between black holes and tepee rings? Stephen Hawking's recent work suggests a new view of the Universe, a continuous succession of universes unending. Black Elk dissects a tiny slice from the grand system and arrives at the same general conclusion. The same principle holds true whether dealing on a cosmic scale or observing the changing seasons from year to year. There's no similarity in phraseology, the methodology couldn't be more diverse, yet the new view seems to parallel the old. Both converge on the concept of perpetual repetitive closed cycles.

We will conclude this Chapter with a final quote from *A Brief History of Time*.

"But if the universe is really completely self-contained, having no boundary or edge, it would have neither beginning nor end: it would simply be. What place, then, for a creator?"

This is indeed a pertinent question, one for which we will seek and find an answer.

> *The unknown is ever a challenge, a call for exploration, a quest for understanding.*

Chapter Six

VISIONS INTO ETERNITY

The First Thought And A Cosmic Coincidence

We in the West seem to insist upon all things having a beginning and an end. Why? Because that is what we see happening all around us every day. The light of dawn follows the darkness of night, spring inevitably yields to winter, birth and life will eventually succumb to death, all the repetitive cycles previously discussed come back to the initial condition. Religion and science perpetuate the idea by speaking of Creation to Armageddon, alpha to omega, big bang to big crunch, and on and on. Is this a universal theme, a hard cruel fact; or could it be otherwise, consciousness forever and universes unending.

We previously observed that two plus two always stack up to four, that the known laws of nature appear immutable, always consistent and reliable. But has this always been true, might there have been a period back in eternity when nature behaved in a random manner? Assuming a continuous succession of universes, can we reasonably conclude that they all conformed to the same rules which we can now identify? Let's consider the possibility that previous universes might have been different, that the laws of nature we now experience may have evolved similar to biological evolution here on Earth.

The last chapter concluded with a statement by Stephen Hawking, "What place, then, for a creator." Let's not dismiss this seemingly heretical statement. Remember, mythology (science and religion) rests upon observation, a sensual appraisal of what we see happening which in turn shapes our perception of reality. But observation and perception are both grounded in the here and now. Cosmologists try to take us back to the first cause and the initial condition which prevailed at the instant of creation. They can take us back a long way, but then the story breaks down at Planck time. This suggests an inconsistency, or inadequacy, in the laws of physics. Hawking's no boundary proposal eliminates the singularity proposition, hence the problem associated with Planck time. It allows contraction to an extremely high density but not total abolition of time and matter. The laws of physics still hold true and another expansion can begin. Hawking said, "it [the universe] would have neither beginning or end, it would simply be."

If Hawking's universe should be the case, previous suppositions concerning time are irrelevant. Spacetime endures through eternity. We could envision eternity as a continuous loop around which spacetime travels, perhaps evolving to higher levels of complexity with each cycle. We could guess that time might become enormously stretched at the end of each cycle, perhaps to the extent as appearing near infinite. The arrow of time would disappear beyond the perceptual horizon, then retreat back to measurable increments as the next expansion began. As endless cycles repeat, time does stretch into eternity. Our perception of a first cause proceeding to catastrophe shatters, figuratively consumed by a black hole. All science and theology predicated upon such a mystical event will also meet the same fate. Our sense of reality goes the same route. In short, do we need a creator if time is eternal?

Eternity Revisited

Just what is eternity? Webster says, among other things: *infinite time; time without beginning or end.* Bringing infinity into the definition is to answer one abstract concept with another—what is infinity.

Eternity and infinity are similar. They do not represent a long period of time or a very large number. They are not a quantity of any sort; they are abstract and intangible concepts. Infinity cannot be calculated*, it is the mortal enemy of mathematicians. Eternity cannot be conceived by earthly minds. This being the case, are we justified in using the term "eternity."

I think so because theoretically the event horizon surrounding a black hole is a small capsule of eternity. If one hovered at precisely the right place, time would stretch into eternity because the gravitational field of singularity would counter, or neutralize, the universal field (zero gravity). It would be a precarious situation requiring delicate maneuvers to account for universal expansion (a weakening of its gravitational field). In theory, eternity can exist for a "time" but what might happen to the black hole during the contraction phase of a universe? For now, however, let's merely think of eternity as something without beginning or end. We will construct a conceptual image of eternity later to

---

*Infinity can be expressed in equation form: $\infty = 1/0$ (one divided by zero). Don't bother to plug this equation into your computer—it would require eternity to complete the computation.

serve as a working symbol, but for now Stephen Hawking's universe beckons our attention.

Universes Without Beginning Or End

Is Hawking's no boundary proposal a possibility? Our perception of reality prompts us to discount such an idea immediately. It goes far beyond our conceptual ability, at least at this point in human history. But before writing off the possibility, consider that Albert Einstein's theories on relativity and Max Planck's quantum mechanics both place severe stress upon our conceptions. Now consider the conceptual advantages of the no boundary model: it eliminates the singularity problem, it avoids the breakdown of physical laws at Planck time, it removes the necessity for a first cause, the initial condition was a previous universe. The three cosmic mysteries of Chapter One disappear. Aside from accepting the idea of physical eternity and removing a creator from the scheme, Hawking's model is more coherent than Big Bang theory.

How do other physicists feel about the proposal? I don't know, for some reason they don't find occasion to correspond with me. That is, I'm not part of the "inner circle" which attends conferences and receives the pertinent literature (it's just as well, I probably wouldn't understand it anyway).

I do know that British physicist Paul Davies, in his book *The Mind of God,*[1] devoted several pages toward giving a graphic image as to how such a model would work. Davies remained rather neutral concerning the no boundary model, but the entire book attempts to convey an objective analysis of physics and metaphysics. The fact that he bothered to explain the model (actually better than did Hawking) implies some degree of acceptance.

I won't take words from Paul Davies' mind, but I personally think we should consider the implications of such a universe. First, we have already concluded that the model circumvents a first cause which in effect alters our concept of what we have termed the Creator. Therefore, the Creator need be something different.

But what?

We can't know although we do sense and experience the presence of a higher intelligence. The recognition of a higher power reaches far back into pre-history and this intuitive knowing became central to all mythologies and religions. The grand mystery is as profound today as it was when Cro-Magnon shamans painted murals on cavern walls some 15,000 years ago. We can't know the nature of the Creator; we can only speculate.

An Evolving Universe

The speculation which follows doesn't portend to convey Absolute Truth, or even probabilities. It's just one way of looking at cosmic evolution regarding the no boundary proposal.

With time reaching back through eternity we can imagine that about anything could happen. Perhaps at some point a spark of consciousness erupted from a void. This First Thought penetrated the chaos of a random universe to lay adjacent to, but beyond the physical realm. This tiny thought survived the tremendous force of compression (as allowed by the no boundary proposal) and continued into the next expansion. We know from personal experience that one thought generates another and that eventually a pyramid of intelligence takes shape. From this emerges consciousness, an awareness of self and our physical surroundings. The source of a cosmic Mind is certainly more mysterious than the spark which brought life to planet Earth, but perhaps after encountering the physical it followed the same principle as now observed in biological systems—chaos to order, simplicity to complexity. Once established, the infant Mind continued to evolve toward higher states of order.

After countless universal cycles, Mind realized that it was constrained, it couldn't expand beyond itself because chaos still reigned throughout physical systems. It needed more room to grow, but without some rules the physical universe would never behave itself. Rules suggest constants, enduring parameters which survive compression and carry forward into the future. How could Mind force consistency upon the physical?

By an act of will (Mind over matter).

Mind recognized its unity, its oneness. The physical was something else, an additional component which resided adjacent to Mind. Mind invented an abstract concept which we now know as numbers. Mind was one component of being, the physical was the other component. Hence, the numeral 2 became a constant and the simple process of addition became a valuable tool. Elementary arithmetic established one dimensional space which freed Mind to explore its consciousness along infinite avenues of thinking (straight lines going in every direction). Mind discovered that thinking along one line sometimes intersects another line of thinking, that you can arrive at a common conclusion coming from different directions. It also observed that two independent lines of parallel thinking never converge. It became apparent that these phenomena produced a consistency, that with a little practice the end result was predictable—thus came the rules of trigonometry and plane geometry. Mind saw that these ideas were good and retained them for all future universes.

After a few more universal cycles Mind realized that 2 is a magical numeral; that is, $2 + 2 = 4$, it could also multiply 2 times itself and come up with the same result ($2 \times 2 = 4$). The square was extremely important because it allowed Mind to explore much more territory: it now had area (a plane) rather than just a straight line to explore and thus came into being two dimensional space. Moreover, the rules of trigonometry and plane geometry still held true. By imposing these rules upon the physical realm, the chaotic patterns of cosmic evolution took on a semblance of order.

Some more thinking suggested that another quantity must exist between the numerals 2 and 4. Mind had as givens the numerals 1, 2, 4, and an unknown quantity which it designated as x. After some reasoning it became apparent that the problem could be solved in two ways: by simple addition, $1 + 2 = 3$, or by a process of division and subtraction, $1 + x = 4$, which after transposition states that $x = 4 - 1$. Mind rejoiced to discover that algebra went beyond arithmetic as a way of solving number problems. By an act of will Mind imposed mathematics upon physical systems thereby further reducing randomness in successive universal cycles.

The numeral 3 also had some mysterious qualities—three doubled stacked up to six, but when squared the product came to nine. The results of squaring and doubling worked different for three than it had for two. What's going on here Mind asked of itself? After wandering around on its square plane for awhile, it looked up in desperation, and lo, space existed upward from the plane. Doing some measurement, Mind defined three dimensional space which it described as a cube. To find its specific quantity, Mind determined that it must multiply 3 x 3 x 3 which comes out to be three times the amount of the sum of the three numbers. By devising an irrational number which it called pi, Mind rounded off the sharp corners of space forming a sphere which was much less cumbersome than a cube.

Mind, like all those which followed, developed curiosity to the extent that it wondered what had happened in the past and what might happen in the future. After some deliberation, Mind reasoned that if time became an inseparable component of three dimensional space, the past may reveal itself and that the future might be anticipated. It was so willed—spacetime became a fixed condition. As expected, Mind now had memory of past events and could predict future possibilities based upon previous experience. This was a momentous breakthrough, in a twinkling Mind transformed itself into Super-Consciousness.

Looking backward in time, Super-Consciousness recoiled at the chaos which reigned. Something needed doing to bring order and uniformity to successive universes. The first step was to bring gravity under control, to impose some standards limiting its erratic behavior. Gravity should be omnipresent in all future universes, but the strength of its force field should diminish with distance. That is, if during the expansion phase two galaxies doubled the distance between themselves the force of mutual attraction should decrease four-fold (as now dictated by the inverse square law). The imposition of this idea produced a more uniform distribution of matter, it also extended the life cycle of each universe.

After a few more universal cycles Super-Consciousness developed a desire to penetrate the darkness of spacetime, to see what was happening. This required some thought. It became apparent that matter needed some rules, some immutable laws which eliminated the random interaction between particles. And that control must begin at the elemental level—in the nucleus of atoms. Two rules would do the job quite well. Immediately after imposing the weak and strong force, thermonuclear reactions ignited in the core of billions of stars and there was light. This brightness, the radiance of the cosmos, needed a distribution system to carry photons and other radiation to the far reaches of spacetime. Implementation of the electromagnetic field handled the task nicely. Thus the basic foundation of physical being came into existence for universes such as we now see. After a period of fine-tuning, these laws found expression in consistent analytical procedures (mathematics now included calculus) which carried forward into perpetuity.

After countless universal generations Super-Consciousness yearned to join physical matter in some temporal arrangement. It directed a splinter, or spark, of itself into inanimate matter. Atoms organized into molecules, molecules joined to form microorganisms, these evolved into conscious thinking creatures who ask difficult questions of themselves.

Thus through eternity did Super-Consciousness evolve. It continues to grow and expand due to the feedback from biosystems scattered throughout countless universes. Mind over matter became the universal theme. Force fields, morphic fields, silent messengers, by whatever name, they are all components of the Great Mind.

So, what do you think of this imaginary universe? I bet that if Moses had gone to school rather than herding sheep, he would have known about pi and how to square a number. Had he known, Genesis might read differently. On the other hand, Moses gave a pretty good account of Creation given the possibility that a day to the Creator may be equivalent to a billion years as we reckon time.

A Universe By Chance

The no boundary proposal suggests another possible mechanism at work. We noted in the preceding scenario that given an eternity within which to operate, about anything might happen. Could it be that at the beginning of the present expansion everything came together just right to allow an orderly universe as now seen. All the constants and laws of nature fell into place purely by chance. This one in a billion billion long-shot happened to contain conditions favoring the evolution of biological systems. Since our present existence is a fluke, it's not certain that life and consciousness will ever appear again.

This possibility not only removes the necessity for a creator, it discounts any hint of a sublime consciousness. We are just here, intelligence is an accident of nature, creation is mere chance.

But wait. Before the atheists jump up in applause, let's take another look at eternity. Perhaps there is a subtle quality about it that we haven't recognized.

As stated earlier, eternity is an abstract concept— a product of the mind. And as we shall see in the next chapter, mind is one aspect of consciousness. It therefore follows that eternity comes into being simultaneous with the emergence of consciousness. Without a contemplative mind, who or what would recognize such an obscure concept? Mind is a prerequisite for eternity.

So, a universe by chance can't happen until Mind

first comes into being, then consciousness evolves through eternity to perfect creation. (I recognize the numerous weak links in the preceding chain of reasoning).

A simple mental exercise might help bring an abstract concept into concrete reality.

Visual Eternity

The circle used to construct a visual representation of a closed cycle (last chapter) also provides a visual device to conceive eternity. By looking at that circle, or thinking of the birds nests and tepee rings in Black Elk's myth, it's readily apparent that the circumference is without beginning or end. Circles just go around and around for as long as anyone wishes to trace the circumference. One could select any tepee in the ring to start an exploration of Black Elk's village, but that tepee has no more significance than any other tepee. Any could be the starting place, but once started, one could walk the circle through eternity without finding the end of the village.

A circle is easy to draw: just stick the sharp end of a compass into a piece of paper, place the pencil end on the paper, and rotate the compass 360 degrees. Lo, there's a circle, a geometric design easily defined as a closed line with all points equidistant from a common point.

But consider the case of a careless draftsman. If he or she lifts the pencil off the paper after completing only 359 degrees, the circle would not close. There would be a starting point and an ending point. It would be a near-miss situation similar to the flat universe model discussed in Chapter One. A little mistake in the other direction would be inconsequential. Rotating the compass 361 degrees would not only close the circle, one could rotate the compass into eternity and not change the character of the circle—although one might need the full time service of a pencil factory to keep the cycle going.

Now comes the essence of the situation: one has to make a conscious decision to construct a circle, then a deliberate action takes place when rotating the compass, and finally, intelligence is necessary to assure at least a 360 degree rotation. It's an act of will. Its success requires knowledge. When complete, one has created visual eternity.

In this case, eternity does not come into being spontaneously; it's not a free lunch, something from nothing as implied by the Universe springing forth from singularity. It can only exist after the execution of a conscious decision on the part of an intelligent creator. Eternity must first come into being before any physical process or system can participate. This, then, is that place for a Creator. We have an answer to Stephen Hawking's question; however, this Creator doesn't initiate a first cause, He/She functions as a mental innovator.

For the sake of *consistency*, we will continue use of the word Creator while recognizing that intelligence must have existed before anything material came into being. We can't know from whence came the Creator, we can only know that a vast and complex system came into being. Though we have a cursory understanding of the natural laws governing physical matter, we are almost totally ignorant concerning the laws which prevail in the spiritual realm (however, we will speculate concerning spiritual imperatives in following chapters). Most of our profound questions remain in the realm of the Absolute Unknowable.[2] However, we do receive subtle messages from the other side, brief glimpses brought to us by silent messengers.

So here we stand, at one instant in eternity, asking from whence we came and worried about where we will go. If our perception allowed us to see and understand the broad spectrum of becoming and being, we might conclude that such questions are irrelevant. We just are, always have been, and will continue as a mental reflection of the Great Mind.

The Here And Now

In a practical sense, it matters not whether the Big Bang, the no-boundary proposal, or another model directs the physical universe. The here and now is our present concern.

How do we fit into the scheme, what about our personal path for life? Lots of questions, not many answers. We seem drawn back to Chapter Four and O'Leary's force fields, Sheldrake's morphic fields, silent messengers, all of which suggest a tacit intelligence which forms the foundation of becoming and being.

Sheldrake's hypothesis holds that form and behavior among species and individuals accumulates with time, that habits (and knowledge) resonate from the past to become a pattern for the present. Put in a slightly different reference, we might say that a subtle consciousness leads species and individuals forward. It's an evolutionary process, ever accelerating, always proceeding from randomness to complexity—from the aimless drifting of microbes in ancient seas to conscious thinking creatures who make plans for today and the future. O'Leary's force fields might be the media, or distribution system, through which this information propagates. I postulated that silent messengers might be a pseudonym applicable to both force and morphic fields, but that they also had the ability to foretell the future to a limited degree. We seemingly left the Creator idle in the midst of His/Her Universe while the hustle and bustle of becoming and being hurried along a purposeful and coherent path.

We now have cause to think that if there is such a thing as a purposeful and coherent path, it didn't come into being spontaneously as in a Universe by Chance. Purpose is a function of mind, of intent, action initiated by intelligence. Coherence comes from experience. With eternity at His/Her disposal, the Creator had/has plenty of time to perfect Creation. He/She is not static, unchanging, following a preordained cosmic blueprint; the Creator is also evolving toward higher realms of consciousness, never resting and always ascending.

Morphic fields, force fields, silent messengers, all are whispers from eternity. The universal data bank can more properly be thought of as the Great Mind, the Source of all knowledge and wisdom, a Grand Spring from which physical creation flowed by an act of divine will. Put another way, the physical realm is a reflection of the spiritual realm, a thought made manifest. Fragments of knowledge, inspiration, and love from spirit filter through an invisible barrier to influence the physical. The phenomena discussed in Chapter Four seems intangible proof of a preexisting intelligence which directs physical systems. It's a mental connection, consciousness nourished by Super-Consciousness.

Back To The Old View

I've withheld an important part of Black Elk's life-story until now. Neilhardt's book, *Black Elk Speaks*, not only portrays the Plains Indian's traditions, its foremost value is a vision which came to Black Elk during his youth, a vision into the Land of Spirit.

Black Elk relates that by the age of four he was hearing voices, voices coming from unseen persons (silent messengers?). He was afraid to tell his parents, not even his grandfather with whom he had a special rapport. He thought the people would laugh and think him crazy. Then the voices diminished as he grew a little older and began learning the ways of a hunter. Suddenly, at age nine, he became gravely ill and fell into a deep coma. Near death, his parents distraught, Black Elk lay still and silent for twelve days.

No man was ever more spiritually alive than Black Elk during those twelve days. His grand vision began much the same as what is now known as a near death experience (discussed in the next section). At some point during the coma two warriors descended from the sky, each with a bolt of lightning in hand. They motioned that he follow. He floated upward on a cloud, and looking back, saw his sick body laying in the tepee below.

Told in the vernacular of his culture, Black Elk reports coming to a tepee in the Spirit World where he came before six wise and ancient Grandfathers. The book contains the entire vision as related to Neilhardt. It's much too detailed and symbolic to go into here, but in short, Black Elk received the powers of a shaman and the insight of a prophet. He became an inspiration for his people through troubled times. The following quote comes from near the end of his mystic vision, he seeing himself standing on the summit of Mt. Harney in the Black Hills of South Dakota, a most sacred site of the Sioux.

"... I stood there [and] I saw more than I can tell and I understand more than I saw; *for I was seeing in a sacred manner* the shapes of all things in the spirit and the shape of all shapes as they must live together like one being. And I saw that the sacred hoop of my people was one of many hoops that made one circle, wide as daylight and as starlight, and *in the center grew one mighty flowering tree to shelter all the children of one mother and one father.* And I saw that it was holy." [all italics are mine].

The Lakota medicine man peered into eternity and the mighty flowering tree he saw at the center was Unity (Unity is defined in Chapter Eight). One doesn't need be a Sioux Indian to perceive the validity of his message. Its fundamental truth is cross-cultural, it has prevailed since times in antiquity. It is as true now as when the first Neanderthal man or woman gazed into the night sky in reverence of the Great Spirit.

Near Death Experiences

Black Elk's vision was not unique. Mythology is alive with such accounts; and they still exist today. Similar experiences occur almost daily, and though they may contain different phraseology, all are of similar content.

Consciousness, mental awareness, or however one chooses to describe nonphysical experiences represent one of the great mysteries of life. Mental acuity and the power of observation exist independent of the physical body. It's as if mind, consciousness, and memory have unlimited freedom; they can disengage from the body in an instant. If trauma, illness, or states of near death as in Black Elk's vision befall one, consciousness withdraws from the physical body to become a mere observer. If and when physical symptoms disappear and the body returns to normal, mental functions return to record and interpret the experiences of life. It often happens that those who suffered what we might describe as an unconscious condition retain a memory of the events which transpired while the body was in a comatose state.

Specific examples are the *near death experiences* (NDSs) studied by practicing psychiatrist, Dr. Raymond A. Moody, Jr. Moody startled both the public and the medical profession in 1975 with publication of his book, *Life After Life*,[3] in which he coined the term NDE. This book, together with two later books, *Reflections on Life After Life*, 1977, and *The Light Beyond*, 1988, describe the experience of several hundreds of patients who suffered clinical death, then recovered following resuscitation.

After a short period of early skepticism, *Life After Life* inspired several other researchers to investigate the field of NDEs. Interest in near death experiences spread world-wise. Physicians around the globe began interviewing those who had clinically died, then came back to life. These independent studies verify Moody's initial work (results reviewed in *The Light Beyond*).

Clinical death resulting from severe injury or cardiac arrest occurs when heartbeat and other vital signs cease to function. In past times, clinical death was usually terminal—one was simply a goner. Now, however, with immensely improved medical equipment and procedures, coupled with rapid transit to emergency facilities, many terminal conditions are reversible. The clinically dead, after resuscitation, come back to life. Some have extremely interesting experiences to relate.

Dr. Moody, in *The Light Byond*, outlines nine traits which characterize a full-blown NDE episode. In his words, "Some [people] might have one or two, others five or six [of these traits]." During the course of his continued study he has interviewed more than a thousand persons who experienced a full-blown episode. Briefly summarized, according to Moody, an NDEer will have the sensation of leaving their body and floating upward toward the ceiling. While in this state all pain ceases, they have an overpowering sense of peace, they can hear and remember everything said and done during the resuscitation effort. They then enter a dark tunnel and move swiftly toward a light at the end. An unknown being sometimes escorts them, and upon emergence from the tunnel they find themselves in a beautiful setting surrounded by creatures of light. They seem able to communicate mentally and frequently find themselves in the presence of departed friends and loved ones. Some meet, in Moody's terms, a Being of Light who assists in a review of their life on Earth, and who sometimes gives them the choice of staying in spirit or returning to physical life. Others are not given this option because their physical time on Earth is incomplete. They return to awake back in their physical body.

Obviously, those given the option elected to come back. Some did so because of having small children to raise, or other responsibilities. Others felt their life's work yet unfinished. Nearly all remember the experience as beautiful and serene.

Most NDEers express profound changes in their outlook on life after recovery. They have lost any fear of death; they sense a two-fold purpose in life, that being an acute desire to learn to love and an unrelenting thirst for knowledge.

Many of Dr. Moody's respondents expressed a sense of timelessness during their NDE. The duration of their experience consumed only minutes as we measure time, yet the events they describe might require hours or days using physical communication methods. This appears to validate our earlier observation that time is meaningless beyond the confines of space and matter. Eternity has no boundaries, no limits, no restrictions; it is expansive and all inclusive. We recall that Black Elk was comatose twelve days during his period of illness, so again, earthly time seems entirely irrelevant in the spiritual dimension.

Portions of Black Elk's vision fit the characteristics of a NDE as described by Dr. Moody. He rose from his body and was met by two entities descending from above. They elevated him to an exalted place, he entered a tepee where six Great Grandfathers (Beings of Light?) offered counsel, the wise ones revealed the knowledge of spirit. Black Elk's semantics differ from Moody's subjects because each vision conforms to the terms used in one's culture.

The details of near death experiences seem to parallel a person's life history and background; personality creeps into the experience, the daily concerns of life enter into the decision whether or not to return. One's cultural background, and/or religious beliefs, also influence the specific traits of near death experiences. Black Elk expressed his vision in terms of tribal customs and beliefs, modern NDEers usually relate their experience in terms of their life circumstance. Such differences are not significant because the human mind attempts to interpret such visions in terms of the familiar, in a way that relates to life's experiences.

One glaring discrepancy distinguishes Black Elk's vision from those of modern day NDEs. His viewpoint was inclusive. That is, Black Elk spoke of his people, the hoop of the tribe, the hoop of the Sioux nation and the great hoop of all nations in the world. Such was his cultural tradition. In contrast, the vision of modern day NDEers is usually personal and exclusive. Though departed friends and relatives may be present, the life review, the meeting with the Being of Light, and the choice to return all involve the individual. The circle, the hoop of all people, the bringing together is absent.

This difference in vision content may relate to the Western tradition which places much emphasis on the soul, particularly its salvation. In the West, religion presumes that mankind is inherently evil, that the purpose of life is to restore grace, to earn forgiveness and redemption. This philosophy focuses on the individual, it separates man from his Creator, the Creator from his Creation.

In contrast, Native American Indian beliefs, and many other primitive cultures, burst forth from Spirit. Their concept of the Great Spirit is inclusive where animals and even mountains and rivers and rocks have spirit. Primitive fundamentalists see themselves, not so much as an individual, but rather a small part of the greater whole. They group all things together and spirit is the cohesive or binding force. (When we speak of primitive peoples, remember that the root word is *prime*, meaning first in time, or original).

Now hear the good news.

Spontaneous Visions

One need not be near death or undergo resuscitation to see into eternity! Very ordinary people can and do receive life transforming visions. Siddhartha Gautama began life as an ordinary man (actually, he was a prince, but without mystic abilities) in an obscure region of India. He went on a long vision quest, and while meditating under a bo-tree he received the enlightenment which brought him fame as the Buddha. Some five hundred years later Jesus of Nazareth was born into an ordinary family (virgin births are common throughout mythology). His vision quest involved forty days of fasting in the wilderness during which he resisted several temptations. The apostle Paul, while traveling the road to Damascus, experienced a vision of brilliant light (Jesus) which left him blinded for three days (recorded in Acts). About five hundred years after Jesus, a bedouin herdsman named Mohammed received a series of visions from which he formulated the Islamic Koran.

Paranormal visions can come to anybody, the achievement of ecclesiastic status is unnecessary. People from all walks of life, through a broad cultural spectrum, receive spontaneous visions or insights. More and more people are stepping forward to relate vivid dreams or mystical impressions received either spontaneously or while in deep meditation or prayer. Such visions are usually inspirational, but recipients often have trouble interpreting the meaning of mystic visions. They must speculate concerning their source, they might question the validity of their vision. They sometimes can't decide whether they are real, or fabrications of the imagination. All too often they keep it to themselves hoping to avoid skepticism and ridicule.

It's small wonder that they become confused. As mentioned, traditional Western religion focuses primarily upon the soul. This leaves us devoid of literature and customs relating to spirit. (Medieval church authorities suppressed paranormal experiences declaring them as being demonic). Now, however, with relaxation of archaic intolerances, spiritual impressions are becoming more abundant. And without historic precedents, we must wander in a spiritual no-man's-land.

Each experience, each exploration is a step into the unexpected, into the unknown.

Until recently, if one happened to undergo a paranormal experience they began to doubt their sanity, and they certainly kept it to themselves. So, imagine the consternation suffered by a highly respected physician when he himself underwent a spontaneous vision in the nineteenth century. Richard M. Bucke, a Canadian of English ancestry, was a scholar, a psychologist, and physician of considerable repute. He had a brilliant mind, and considering the prevailing attitudes at the time, he was most assuredly a rebel thinker. His vision occurred at age thirty-six while visiting in England. The following is a partial description of his experience, he, speaking in the third person:

> "He [Bucke speaking of himself] was in a state of quiet, almost passive enjoyment. All at once, without warning of any kind, he found himself wrapped around as it were by a flame-colored cloud. For an instant he thought of fire, some sudden conflagration in the great city; the next, he knew that the light was within himself. Directly afterwards came upon him a sense of exultation, of immense joyousness accompanied or immediately followed by an intellectual illumination quite impossible to describe. Into his mind streamed one momentary lightning-flash of the Brahmic Splendor which has ever since lightened his life, upon his heart fell one drop of Brahmic Bliss, leaving thence-forward for always an aftertaste of heaven. ... He claims that he learned more within the few seconds during which the illumination lasted than in previous months or even years of study, and he learned much that no study could have ever taught." [From *Cosmic Consciousness*, note 4, below].

As with Dr. Moody's NDEers, Bucke's life underwent transformation as a result of the illumination. His inquisitive mind demanded an explanation of the experience. He methodically studied the esoteric literature of East and West. He searched for and found others having had similar experiences. Nearly 30 years of research went into his book, *Cosmic Consciousness*,[4] published in 1901. Bucke's work received instant acclaim from American physician and philosopher William James and Russian mathematician and philosopher P.D. Ouspensky. Ironically, less than a year after publication of *Cosmic Consciousness*, Bucke stepped out on his veranda to view the stars. He slipped on a patch of ice and fell which resulted in a fatal head injury.

Cosmic Consciousness contains a review of 14 historic persons who, in Bucke's opinion, experienced the cosmic illumination, plus 36 others of lesser, imperfect, or doubtful instances. Considering the difference in circumstances, the illumination described by Bucke is compatible with the NDEs recorded by Raymond Moody. The death and resuscitation scenes are obviously absent in Bucke's work, but the bright light and/or sudden knowing always comes through whatever the experience. Bucke viewed his experience as a spiritual encounter; Moody, being a practicing professional, follows a conservative approach typical of scientific investigation. Regardless of interpretation, Moody seems to have few if any reservations concerning the validity of the near death experience.

Richard Bucke emerged from his vision a transformed person. Surprised and astounded, Bucke sought an explanation for that which the Western tradition had long held heretical. Dr. Raymond Moody's pioneering work surprised both the public and the medical community. Black Elk was neither surprised by his vision, nor did he consider it paranormal.

A deliberate vision quest by young men was an integral part of most Indian tribal customs. For many tribes, it was a part of the initiation ceremony celebrating the transition to manhood. Their spiritual beliefs came in large part from the content of past visions. The Indian tradition was fluid and dynamic, subject to either change or elaboration dependent upon new information or wisdom resulting from visions quests. Black Elk regarded his vision as spiritual truth; he followed his myth to the end of life without question or doubt.*

The idea of a vision quest is not alien to many Westerners today. Some go to church, some meditate, some receive spontaneous impressions. However received, visions are valid, brief glimpses into eternity.

Immortal Consciousness?

Are brief visions into eternity proof of immortality? Not so according to the atheist, and not by following current scientific methodology. But the preceding body of accumulating psychological evidence suggests an emphatic "yes." Both the theist and the metaphysician will accept such a conclusion without qualification.

I don't know whether I qualify as either a theist or metaphysician in the strictest sense, but I do think that consciousness survives senility and death even though the physical body decomposes to its initial condition. Symbolically, physical death is synonymous with the Big Crunch or the terminal stage of compression as in the no boundary model: a return to the initial con-

---

*Black Elk did join the Catholic Church. Some think he did so to allay the persecutions imposed by missionaries who in effect dictated reservation policies.

dition where the physical body degrades back to molecules and atoms and consciousness returns to Spirit (its initial condition) to reside through eternity.

After the terminal event of one universe, another Big Bang or expansion might produce a new universe, and though being similar, it would not be the same universe as the one in which we now reside. Likewise, we could reasonably expect other humans and creatures to evolve. Here again, new but different lives may be similar to what we now see on Earth, but they will not be the *same* individuals. One's soul, after returning to Spirit, is what survives through eternity.

Coincidences seem to just happen. We usually think of them as when two seemingly related events occur near simultaneously at different localities. An act of Providence is generally considered divine intervention into the affairs of man. Silent messengers flutter back and forth from the spiritual to the physical carrying insights and knowledge.

Now, how do you distinguish one from another? I don't know, but here's something for you to ponder. Richard Bucke received his illumination while visiting England in the spring of 1872. Black Elk, near death in a tepee somewhere in Sioux territory, had his great vision just a month or three later, in the summer of 1872!*

---

*British physicist David Bohm would likely discount the probability of coincidence. Instead, he might argue that these two events are quite rational, being an expression of what he calls "the implicate order" (Re: his book, *Wholeness and the Implicate Order*, 1980). This phenomenon might also fit the concept of physics known as nonlocality, two corresponding events separated by space. I personally don't consider these two events coincidental—something strange is going on, perhaps another component of the cosmic imperative which pushes complex systems toward higher states of order.

> *Mysteries are the spice of life—for*
> *if we knew all the answers,*
> *how dull and boring our existence?*

Chapter Seven

UP THE LADDER TOWARD SPIRITUALITY

The Physical—The Metaphysical

Our world is full of mystery. We trouble our minds with concerns about origins, destiny, the material aspects of life. We become so preoccupied with thinking about external things that we neglect, or even forget about, internal things. We too often lose sight of the internal mysteries, like what motivates us, why are we so curious, so inquisitive? Why do we have this unrelenting desire to know, why do we sense a higher purpose?

These mysteries are like an echo from beyond, a subtle reminder that the inner-self needs more attention. We tend to forget that it's the inner-self which leads us forward, which exists both internally and external. It plays a dual role: it maintains health and a sense of physical well-being; perhaps more important, it produces feelings such as desire, inspiration, hope, compassion, love. The inner-self is a residual shadow of the Great Mind, a presence which penetrates to the core of Being.

We must now confront the mystery within, that submerged knowing and yearning which, like our own shadow, stalks us through life.

Unconscious Knowing

Intellectual acuity can propel us through many of life's situations, the external things. It falls short when contemplating internal mysteries; for instance, how do we sometimes know who's calling even before answering the telephone? Or how, when driving a narrow winding road, do we sometimes receive a sudden flash of knowing that another vehicle is about to come around the bend? Or why, after dreaming of a place, many years later we actually visit it in physical reality?

Other mysteries come to mind. Where are memories stored and how can many of us remember things that never happened in this lifetime? Where, and how, do ideas germinate? What's the difference between thinking and daydreaming, between knowing and believing? Are some of those confined to mental institutions any more insane than the rest of society? Where is the mind seated and how does it operate? What is reality, and why do we search for a higher meaning in life?

The metaphor relating to silent messengers and the universal data bank serves as a way of knowing various things, but as with force fields and morphic fields, it tells us nothing about *why* we want to know. We sense the great mystery, it wells up from the inner-self like a perennial spring. We subconsciously know that the inner-self is not content to meander through life eating and drinking, building a fortune, and leaving behind a large estate. It has a higher mission, a goal which we will call the quest for Spiritual Awareness.

The Twin Components of Being

Being a professional engineer all my life, I've always thought of myself as an analytical person: Newton's physics rest at the core of all things physical, every action has a cause, every cause demands action. All material questions are answerable through reason by applying well established scientific principles. It works quite well for mechanical things like windmills and coffee grinders. Take medicine as another example. If one suffers a broken leg, given a cast and several weeks time it will heal; or, if one develops appendicitis, a relatively simple surgical procedure eliminates the problem. Whether it be engineering, medicine, biology, or geology, we are dealing with physical systems—tangible things, the physical aspect of Being.

Trouble comes when we look at the other aspect of Being. Engineers can't build a bridge across the chasm separating now from forever; doctors can't heal a broken heart resulting from the loss of a loved one. Nor can medicine cure the agony of disappointment, or restore lost self-esteem. These burdens fall to the inner-self for resolution. Fortunately, through expanding knowledge, professionals are beginning to recognize the mysteries contained within the inner aspect of Being.

Our world-view began changing in the 1960s. That decade brought in civil liberties and other significant social changes. Just as important, and much more sublime, the next decade produced an explosion of new knowledge and information concerning the cosmos and human consciousness. Professionals from many disciplines began writing books and giving lectures comprehensible to the average lay-person. Newton's physics and Freud's psychology slipped into the background of human curiosity. We had new tools with which to understand ourselves.

When we came to understand the implications of general relativity, Newton's universe shrank to the size of the solar system. Carl Jung had long since parted philosophical company with his mentor Sigmund Freud, and from Jung came a new way of viewing the human psyche. Next came (not necessarily in chronological order) Robert Monroe[1] describing out of body experiences, Raymond Moody and his near death experiences, another edition of Richard Bucke's work hit the street, Carlos Castaneda[2] upset our conventional view of reality, Dick Sutphen[3] introduced us to past-life hypnotic regressions. Former astronaut Edgar Mitchell[4] founded an institute to study mind and consciousness. These are a mere sampling of the information which came during the 1970s and '80s. This new knowledge revealed the inner-Being, it comprising an inseparable part of the physical.

Combining The Physical With The Metaphysical

It's probably apparent that I still give a lot of credence to physics and natural science. I'm still an engineer at heart, but the above works and many others reveal that mainstream science has limitations concerning what it can teach. If one wants answers to profound questions, he or she must venture into the realm of metaphysics. This entire book is an attempt to blend the two, to find the parallels. Physics isn't easy. Metaphysics is mystic and elusive, yet I sense a correspondence between the two.

Physics and metaphysics seem to interact, one lending suport to the other, both moving in the same direction leading toward a common denominator. They appear as symmetrical partners, each having similar characteristics, each functioning on a different plane. When combined they constitute the collective whole.

The imaginary universe postulated in the last chapter credited a Great Mind with bringing order to a previously random universe. It did so by establishing constants, by imposing certain rules governing physical matter. Admittedly, it was all a fabrication; but regardless of how the Universe came into being, it is certain that Mind takes precedence over the physical. The four known forces of physics had to have come from a Supreme Intelligence—a universe by chance is unthinkable. The Mind of the Creator evolved through eternity, it achieved perfection before an ordered universe came into being. Mind, then matter, came together forming a universe as now observed.*

Our inner-world is a fragment of the Great Mind. It establishes guidelines for life; the physical body is merely a mechanism. Coming from a high Source, the inner-world complies with spiritual constants. That is, the inner-self follows divine laws; it existed before we came into the physical, it will continue after death into eternity.

Divine law penetrates and governs both components of Being; it provides life directives, it continues to direct an evolving universe. Since Spirit came before the physical, we might reasonably conclude that four basic spiritual energies complement the four known forces of physics. In other words, physical and spiritual laws are symmetrical, with Spirit being dominant in all worlds.

---

*This line of thinking parallels a theory of physics known as the Anthropic Principle which loosely says that the Universe is the way it is because we couldn't be here if it were otherwise.

The Myth Begins

Fig. 7-1 which follows is a schematic depicting four distinct and separate divisions. Within each of the four major categories of Spiritual Energy are three subdivisions. The basic, or fundamental, energies begin at the bottom of the page. Each step up the ladder indicates a higher order of energy, each represents a mystery, each level is more complex than the one below. The assignment of priorities, or orders of importance, is strictly judgemental on my part. And of course, Fig. 7-1 is an analogy, not intended as literal truth.

Beginning at the bottom of Fig. 7-1, we will work our way upward.

PHYSICAL SYSTEMS

Laws Governing Physical Matter

These form the foundation for all which ascends upward into higher realms of Spirit. Included within this group is the intelligence which tells particles of matter how to combine forming quarks, how quarks combine to form atoms. One of these laws would tell atoms how to form molecules, another would tell electrons to avoid each other, yet another would tell a compass needle to point toward the magnetic north pole. Physical law tells gravity, among other duties, to hold us to the ground preventing us from flying off into space. It also told gravity how to shape the Universe. Physical laws governing matter, always reliable (at this point in time), interacting and complementing one another, allow us to make functional automobiles, refrigerators, and video games. These same laws, by way of spiritual imperatives, prohibit the destruction

Spiritual Energies

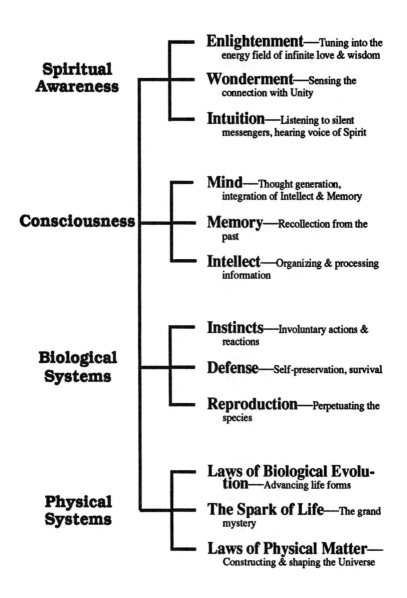

Spiritual Awareness
- **Enlightenment**—Tuning into the energy field of infinite love & wisdom
- **Wonderment**—Sensing the connection with Unity
- **Intuition**—Listening to silent messengers, hearing voice of Spirit

Consciousness
- **Mind**—Thought generation, integration of Intellect & Memory
- **Memory**—Recollection from the past
- **Intellect**—Organizing & processing information

Biological Systems
- **Instincts**—Involuntary actions & reactions
- **Defense**—Self-preservation, survival
- **Reproduction**—Perpetuating the species

Physical Systems
- **Laws of Biological Evolution**—Advancing life forms
- **The Spark of Life**—The grand mystery
- **Laws of Physical Matter**—Constructing & shaping the Universe

Fig. 7-1

of energy. They will allow energy to be converted into matter, and matter into energy, but the balance between energy and matter remains forever the same.

The Spark of Life

Things become increasingly mystic as we move up the ladder. The search for the missing mass is mundane compared to the great mystery of emergent life. Matter is tangible. It is solid, we can hold it in hand, but not so for the Spark of Life. Finding, identifying, or discovering this mystic essence completely eludes science. And it's not because they haven't tried.

Paleontologists, microbiologists, geologists, even cosmologists enter the quest.[5] A lot of elaborate theories abound, many coming from folks with Ph.D. hanging on the end of their names. These theories fail because of science's mechanistic approach; that is, scientists are without means or methods to investigate metaphysical systems (yet).

Science can trace the evidence of life on Earth back 3.5 bilion years or more. It can classify various life forms, generally describe each of their physical appearances, and define the environment in which life existed. But they don't know how it all started, they can't create life from inanimate matter. The best we can now say is that the Spark of Life is clearly a spiritual energy. It's an essence which emanates from Spirit to take on physical characteristics.

The emergence of life on Earth leads us back to questions concerning coincidence. Given billions of possibilities, was the emergence of life happenstance, a fluke of nature, a once in eternity occurrence? No, I think not. Life isn't accidental, something strange is going on—hidden order lurks in the background.

Life, even inanimate matter, complies with nature's imperative to self-organize and evolve toward ever more complexity.[6]

Laws Governing Biological Evolution

After coming into the physical, life must adhere to certain spiritual rules. Charles Darwin said that life is a dog-eat-dog situation—survival of the fittest. This isn't always true. Life is intelligent and not completely dependent upon a random process of selection.[7] Life comes into a given situation and then evolves and adapts accordingly, and when necessary, life sometimes takes charge by molding the environment to suit its requirements (an example, the oxygen revolution some 2 million years ago).

Biological evolution is a process of growth, advancement and improvement. Each new species is an improvement, a higher form than previous species (capitalizing on past experience contained within morphic fields). Each successive species is more complex, better able to adapt to its environment, more capable of controlling its circumstances. Life is smart, it receives instructions from a high Source (silent messengers). And the further the system progresses, the faster the improvements come. Biological evolution is always ascending, improving toward what we know not. Maybe even Spirit doesn't know where biological life may go next, but we can know that Spirit will mysteriously guide living systems in a positive direction.

We have more to say about the dynamics driving biological evolution in a later subsection.

BIOLOGICAL SYSTEMS

Reproduction and Replication

Given the existence of life, the system governing the perpetuation of species requires specific instructions, a built-in knowledge (morphic fields) emanating from Spirit via silent messengers (morphic resonance). Life is indeed unique to the physical realm because of its ability to replicate and reproduce. A rock can't hatch another rock even though it may lay in a bed of abundant material. A supernova can transform matter, but it can't replicate itself. A wild river may appear alive and vibrant, but its continued existence depends upon climate and not anything it does itself.

The underlying secret of continuing life is the ability of a cell to make an exact copy of itself and divide. This knowledge came with the first cell that ever came into being. Though primitive in origin, this process is still fundamental to growth and maintenance of self in every microbe, every blade of grass, every moving creature. Even as you read this page, your body will manufacture thousands of new cells to replace those which die or become injured.

As seen in Chapter Two, it took a very long time for multicellular organisms to appear. But once life mastered the ability to produce ever more complex DNA molecules, the faster advanced life forms arrived. Cell division alone became inadequate in itself to bring complex organisms into being. The evolutionary process required that advanced organisms start from an infantile state. Reptiles, birds, and fish bring the components of life together in an egg, which when hatched, brings an immature but complete creature into being. Mammals use a more elaborate system which employs fetus growth within the protection of a womb.

With few exceptions, reproduction requires a duality involving a sexual partnership to bring about fertilization of the female egg or blossom by the male sperm or pollen.* The fertilization or pollination process is extremely selective. Every seed, spore, egg, and sperm knows its mission. Pollen from a fir tree will not fertilize the seed of an elm, monkeys and pigs can't produce a cross-breed, a rainbow trout can't fertilize the spawn of a bass. Every species has access to unique intelligence (morphic fields), each is exclusively partial to its own kind.** Without conscious action, every life form serves self and its species as a whole. Somehow, silent messengers guide and direct the reproduction process.

Defense and Self-preservation

Morphic resonance takes an active role in the preservation of species. Silent messengers, aware of past problems and the ways of survival under adverse circumstances, guide each species toward their optimum niche in an ecosystem. This subtle intelligence is nature's way of taking care of its creatures.

Nature, via morphic resonance, endows every creature with the physical traits needed for Self-preservation. Such traits include natural weapons such as fang and claw and tusk, fleetness of foot or wing, camouflage coloration, or the ability to survive in an environment hostile to creatures of prey. Further aiding survival, the creatures of nature instinctively cooperate with one another because if Darwin's world prevailed only one

---

*Asexual reproduction does occur in a few plants and lower species.
**The mothering instinct is something of an exception—a hen chicken rearing a brood of ducklings for instance.

species might survive—which in turn would lead to self-destruction.

This spiritual imperative is clearly evident in pristine forests which harbor a wide assortment of animals and plants. To avoid competition for resources, each species adopts a different method of survival. Somehow, the animals in a given ecosystem develop dietary habits different from other species to avoid depleting various links in the food-chain. As an example, the forests near where I live teem with wildlife, yet I rarely see a heavy winter kill. The prime reason is that deer predominantly browse, elk prefer to graze, bears hibernate during winter then become omnivorous after emerging in the spring, the few moose hang along the creek bottoms eating water loving plants, squirrels eat the nuts and cones of trees, birds eat berries and insects and worms, the fish in streams eat insects, under-water grubs, plankton, and each other. Rabbits eat grass, coyotes and birds of prey eat rabbits. Cougars eat small game and the young and feeble of large game. The system remains balanced until something (usually man) disrupts the ecosystem in which they all live.

Plant life has mechanisms to protect the individual and assure the preservation of species. Some develop thorns and spikes, others produce toxic resins or foliage, some thrive in places inaccessible to most herbivorous feeders. Seeds are extremely vulnerable to predation; however, some plants take advantage of predators by having its seeds propagated in the feces of those they feed. A few biologists speculate that high mountain lakes became stocked with fish because of birds carrying in and depositing fertilized eggs in the shallow waters along shore-lines. Again, interdependency among species, cooperation to assure the survival of all.

Many species over-produce seeds and eggs to compensate for low germination efficiency and/or high mortality rates among off-spring. A female salmon lays a thousand eggs or more in a spawn but probably not over a half-dozen will survive to maturity. Small animals such as rabbits and mice give birth to large litters because of high mortality throughout life; in contrast, deer and elk having fewer predators produce singles and sometimes twins (triplets are rare). Germination efficiency for botanical life is even less successful. Each plant or tree may produce thousands of seeds and often not a single one will sprout and grow to become a mature plant. The single exception might be the dandelions in my lawn.

Instincts

Self-defense is an instinct. So is the urge to procreate. Both satisfy the biological urge to perpetuate the species. Perhaps morphic fields contain the essential information, or maybe silent messengers retrieve and disseminate that which each individual should know. Whichever, instincts are ever alert, always on duty, always ready to issue the proper command.

Aiding survival, all creatures instinctively demand an exclusive domain, termed *The Territorial Imperative* by Robert Ardrey.[8] We've known since youth that a cornered animal is a dangerous animal. Park Rangers and back-country outfitters admonish visitors and clients to give nature's creatures plenty of space. It's good advice. It is rare when a wild one will attack a human, but go on guard if you come between a sow bear and her cubs, or challenge a bull moose for the trail. Even a house cat, if threatened, will take a defensive stand if backed into a corner. Each creature of nature has its territory, an exclusive domain which they will fight to defend (mankind more than other species).

Instincts are something we know without knowing that we know. They exist as an external field of knowledge having a direct connection to the brain and central nervous system. Instinct leaps into action when most needed, it keeps us out of trouble, it leads us in the proper direction, it protects the individual and preserves the species. Fortunate for man, who likes to analyze a situation and ask numerous questions, instinctive reaction is automatic—acting without thinking. This time saving response prevents a lot of accidents which might have already happened if we took time for analysis.

Instincts are similar to Intuition which we discuss later, but there is a subtle difference. Instincts are involuntary reactions usually involving physical action, a doing of something without thinking. Intuition is a knowing, a conscious awareness, which may or may not activate motion or action. Human animals seem to have forfeited some primitive instincts as a result of increasing ability to reason and analyze. When thinking replaces instincts, intuition then steps in as another way of knowing.

In Chapter Four we discussed animals uncanny ability to anticipate future weather conditions. We credited silent messengers with having that ability. They informed the wild ones that it was time to return to their summer grounds even though the calendar would suggest otherwise. The robins and geese knew something that I didn't need to know because my species has learned to control its environment. Sunshine or snow, I'll still be comfortable. But not so for other creatures of nature, they must rely upon basic instincts to survive.

CONSCIOUSNESS

It's easy to speak of consciousness, it's something else to say what it includes. Philosophers and psychologists have long pondered the nature of consciousness. They ask: what is reality?, what is imaginary?, is individuality an illusion?, do I really exist, or is life merely a dream? They provide many questions, few answers.

Natural science does no better. Until recently all branches of science operated from the premise that consciousness is unique to mankind—that its existence is what separates man from the apes. That is, consciousness is what makes us human. This tacit assumption became a cornerstone of reason when fledgling anthropologists began classifying the fossilized remains of primitive human-like creatures first discovered in Western Europe during the nineteenth century (Neanderthal man). Initial investigations centered around comparative skeletal anatomy. Then as more and more specimens were discovered, anthropologists focused increasingly upon evidence suggestive of spoken language (limited to comparative anatomy) and the improved development and use of tools. Thus, to be human required verbal communication and the conscious application of tools to satisfy a predetermined objective.

The years following World War II witnessed a flurry of archaeological activity throughout the Old World (Europe, Asia, and Africa). Older and older fossils were recovered, going backward in time to *Home erectus, Homo habilis,* and finally to *Australopithecus* first discovered in Africa by Raymond Dart in the 1920s. The language and tool use hypothesis began crumbling because it became evident that even *H. habilis* was a maker and user of tools. Moreover, during the 1970s other evidence (preserved foot prints discovered by Mary Leakey) suggested that *Australopithecus* abided by a form of primitive culture (family units). Beyond any doubt, these archaic hominids are neither genetically nor anatomically related to either Neanderthal or modern humans.

So, what next—what is the criteria delineating apes from humans?

A new breed of anthropologists added cognition and culture to the definition of what it takes "to be human."[9] This is certainly a more refined and inclusive way of thinking about human characteristics. But it also topples man from his self-acclaimed pedestal of superiority.

When speaking of cognition and culture we confront the subject of awareness, or taking it a realistic step further, we arrive at consciousness. We don't know much about the lifestyle of *H. habilis* other than he engaged in activities intended to produce a preconceived result (tool use). *H. erectus* went still further: it's generally accepted that he could control fire, that he engaged in some form of ceremony or ritual, and that he was the world's first geographic explorer. Elementary culture including ceremonials, curiosity concerning what lay beyond the horizon, and acts to produce a desired result all bespeak evolving consciousness.

So, now what makes us human?

Not consciousness. It pre-existed our appearance on Mother Earth. Humans are a product of biological evolution; consciousness is an evolving metaphysical energy associated with advanced life forms. We just happen to be at the summit, at least for the present.

Without qualification, we can say that consciousness is something separate from the physical body.

This was clearly evident in the last chapter: the vision into eternity experienced by Black Elk, that by Richard Bucke, the NDEs reported by Raymond Moody. Paleoanthropology provides a sketch of pre-historic consciousness among our ancient ancestors. In all cases we are reading tangible results; but we still don't understand the process, it's still a metaphysical energy.

Accepting the idea that consciousness is transcendental, we can make a short mental list of the things it isn't. First, it is neither physiological nor anatomical. Second, it isn't a quality or personality trait hiding in some remote region within brain matter. Third, it isn't identical between idividuals. What is it then?

As seen, science isn't much help in answering this question. It's true, science during the past two decades made considerable progress concerning the physiology of the brain but it hasn't defined or quantified consciousness. We still ask: where is memory stored, where and how do thoughts originate, where is the physiological seat of the mind? No answers here from science. Lacking a definitive answer, my myth assumes that consciousness, among other things, is a composite blending of *intelligence, memory,* and *mind.* Emotions, learning, involuntary habits, mental disease, hypnotic induced mental states, and other factors also enter the equation somewhere, perhaps as a subtle component of mind.

Despite all the thinking given these uncertainties, it's hard to come up with a comprehensive understanding of consciousness. Webster offers little help: *consciousness:* "the totality of one's thoughts, feelings, and impressions; mind." The last word, *mind,* is at the center of the question, but we are still left in uncertainty—what is mind?

Lower Levels of Consciousness

For a starter, let's approach the question of consciousness from a lower level—using a sleeping dog. While I struggle to find answers to my questions, my golden retriever, Pete, is laying here beside my desk sound asleep totally oblivious to what I am doing. To all outward appearances, he is unconscious, unconcerned, totally out of it. But if I were to jangle the keys to the pickup truck he would instantly jump up and become fully alert. He would perk his ears and cock his head knowing that he would be going somewhere. He wouldn't know where he was going, or why, but nonetheless he would be fully conscious of my every move. In this case consciousness after awakening would be an alertness—a knowing based on past experience that something was impending. But, is Pete aware that he is a dog and I a human, and that our mental process is much different?

He does demonstrate some human characteristics in that he can express love, display compassion, experience emotions. He loves all the little grandchildren who stay with us and will lay quietly beside their crib for hours. He can demonstrate utter dejection when told he has to stay home as the rest of us climb into the pickup (the car is off-limits because the wife objects to wearing a golden fur coat even during winter). And of course, being a hunting dog, he likes birds. But since I don't hunt birds, he doesn't try to retrieve. Instead, he seems infatuated by birds and likes a close association with them.

Pete is a conscious living creature, but the question is: does he possess consciousness as humans experience it? Sure, he has intelligence, he can learn, he has memory, he can express emotion, he has the power of association, he has likes and dislikes. He has the ability to solve simple problems. He demonstrates another human trait in that he obeys when it suits his pleasure, otherwise he acts as if he didn't hear (the wife asserts that he learned this from me). Do these human-like traits constitute consciousness, or does his inability to learn algebra rule out full-blown consciousness?

Pete is a smart dog but I don't think he indulges in abstract thought. Other than occasionally burying a bone for posterity, I don't think he deliberately plans for some future event. I doubt that he envisions someday living in a grand doghouse somewhere in the hereafter. Though he be a good buddy, my mental facilities are far superior to his (I hope he can't read because this statement might hurt his feelings). I know that I know, I know why I do certain things, I analyze and deliberate, I attempt to control the future. Pete takes things pretty much as they come, and for the most part he seems as happy as most humans.

I've made a very simple analogy using a dog, but the example contains an ambiguity. At the onset I assumed that sleep represents a lapse of consciousness. This isn't so. It's apparent that even Pete dreams while sleeping: he will occasionally let out a little yip, or his feet will quiver as if running. Even for a dog, sleep is not a suspension of consciousness, an altered state perhaps, but not a mental black-out.

Few animal lovers would deny their pets some degree of consciousness. Beyond doubt (in my opinion), Pete possesses intellect and memory, albeit at a lower level than mine, or even *Homo habilis*. Does he have a *mind*, the mental ability needed to integrate the functions of intellect and memory? I say yes: the power of association is a product of *mind*—it requires an evaluation of sensual stimulus and recall from memory. Putting memory and anticipation together is a process, and in this case, mind is where it takes place. Pete is a conscious living creature, but his lower level of mental abilities do not come close to being human-like.

A Higher Level of Consciousness

Human consciousness differs from other animals in that we make decisions after subjecting a problem or situation to analysis and deliberation, which usually leads to understanding, creativity, and some degree of control over the future. We are conscious of consciousness, we know that we know, we make plans and carry them out.

Now, getting on with the myth, again refer to Fig. 7-1. As with previous Spiritual Energies, three levels of mental activity comprise Consciousness. What are the three most important components of consciousness? I've already inferred that Intellect, Memory, and Mind constitute the major mental functions. All three are transcendent, Mind of itself represents the collective total of everything mental. It integrates the functions of Intellect and Memory into its total performance, but it also receives subliminal messages from Spirit.

The human species, with its highly evolved consciousness, can say that it knows what it knows, and that it also knows how to use that which it knows. Though the brain and central nervous system are physical components essential to experiencing consciousness, mental states are nonetheless further removed from the physical than the two lower orders of spiritual energy (Physical and Biological Systems). There is nothing material about intelligence, memory is completely intangible, mind is abstract. Physical pain due to disease or injury is very real (although it is often mitigated by the mind); emotions such as distress are feelings generated by sensual stimulus and/or our perception of self-esteem, and though sometimes thought of as painful, they are merely mental products. If the ego is subject to insult, our feelings become hurt but we remain physiologically intact.

The separation of mind from body is clearly evident in medical practice. Psychiatrists and psychologists treat mind and behavior, physicians and surgeons deal with disease and physical impairments.* Though they may overlap in the case of injury to the brain or nervous system, the study of consciousness and behavior remains metaphysical.

Intellect

So, what is Intellect? Let's say that it is Mind's basic information reception and interpreting center. It receives a constant inflow of data such as sensual stimulus, formal learning, conversation, introspection, spontaneous insights, etc. Each incoming signal receives instant evaluation and is then sent to the proper agency, maybe triggering an action or merely sent to memory for future use.

If sensual input identifies a potentially dangerous situation arising, say an oncoming car crossing into our lane of traffic, Intellect instantly generates a multitude of thoughts. The situation requires an immediate decision. Options flood the Intellect. Will the other driver correct his or her course in time to avoid a collision, should I hit the brakes or is there somebody close behind me, can I escape into the borrow-pit or is it

---

*Leading edge psychologists and psychiatrists are moving away from drugs and tranquilizers in the treatment of some mental disorders (treating mind as if it were in the brain). Other forms of therapy, such as hypnosis, often work when other methods fail.

too steep, should I just brace myself for the crash?

In the meantime, Intellect has sent a message to the brain telling it to prepare the body for physical action or possible injury. The entire body reacts. Adrenaline spurts into the blood stream, the pulse and respiratory rate quickens, all physiological systems prepare for an emergency, the psyche prepares to accept imminent injury or death. Some strange thoughts cross the mind, all within a fraction of a second.

Or, we might be listening to a conversation which brings an influx of new ideas. Intellect quickly evaluates and classifies each thought, then sends it to memory for future recall. A quiet time, such as meditation or prayer or introspection, might produce an inspirational insight. Intellect may make multiple use of this perception by sending it to memory and also command brain to produce a state of physical relaxation and a sense of mental well being. And of course, Intellect may become bored with a given situation and switch channels which allows us to day-dream until sensual input turns to something more interesting. Intellect works with blazing speed, processing huge volumes of information every wakeful second of life. No computer can compare to human intellect.

Intellect is not a given, something bestowed at birth which remains static or stable through life. It is not knowledge; it is something acquired, cultivated, and enhanced by life experiences. It searches beyond the horizon when nurtured, it is dynamic and expansive throughout life. The degree of expansion depends upon the desire of the individual, his or her method of thinking, the amount of effort one puts forth. Intellect begins growth at birth. Its rate and extent of growth depends upon one's inherent curiosity, the diversity of one's life experience, the amount of acquired formal learning, and to some extent by those with whom we associate. Open-mindedness is crucial to expanding Intellect, hence stimulating consciousness. Dogmatic beliefs and rigid opinions retard its growth. A formal education certainly assists expansion of the Intellect, but it is not essential (Black Elk, for example). Any observant and open-minded individual can maintain intellectual growth with or without formal credentials—common sense, curiosity, an unrelenting desire to know are of more value than letters behind one's name.

Memory

We will think of Memory as a warehouse of stored information and life experiences. It is the repository for all the labors of Intellect. The two are intertwined, the connection is reciprocal in that Intellect draws knowledge from Memory to assist in the evaluation of new incoming data. It then makes appropriate revisions and returns the upgraded material to Memory. This mental feedback loop, or exchange, keeps Intellect dynamic and Memory's data bank expanding.

Intellect decides which information it accepts and sends to Memory. If the input has little relevance to the interests or desires of an individual, it is soon forgotten. But if it is pertinent to one's curiosity, it will dwell in Memory for a lifetime. Said another way, we remember those things which suit our individual interests or tastes; information outside our area of curiosity stands little chance of long term residency in Memory.

Associations are an inextricable component of the Memory/Intellect partnership. An event or circumstance will trigger reminders of other times when something similar happened. Feelings of joy or sorrow may accompany an association dependent upon our emotions when something similar happened. Feelings of joy or sorrow may accompany an association dependent upon our emotions when something happened in the past. Attending a wedding may remind us of a happy time in life, visiting a sick friend may recall a time when we suffered a problem. Returning to a certain place may recall a previous adventure, seeing a schoolmate will remind us of our youth, hearing a song might bring back a variety of memories and emotions. Animals also have the power of association—remember Pete's reaction at the jingle of pickup keys.

Memory is more mysterious than Intellect; it has power and abilities which transcend the limitations of human thinking and reason. That is, Memory can also function independent of sensual input and conscious learning—brief visions into eternity, for example. Such information is totally dissociated from anything generated by Intellect, it has nothing to do with life experiences.

The strange phenomenon of subconscious knowing only recently received formal recognition within Western psychological practice. In retrospect, it's obvious that it existed throughout the tenure of evolving consciousness (as morphic resonance), but only during the past few decades did it receive clinical verification. Research conclusively reveals that altered mental states produce varied brain wave patterns, or frequencies. As brain wave activity declines, mental states become more subjective until finally one enters the sublime world of dreams. Between normal wakeful consciousness and sleep is where subconscious knowing emerges.

Part of the initial impetus for research into altered mental states came from strange quarters. Most remembered, perhaps, are the so-called flower children of the 1960s and their experiments with psychedelic drugs. Concurrently, yoga and transcendental meditation swept through another segment of emancipated thinkers. And of course, the idea of hypnosis goes back to the mid-eighteenth century work of Viennese physician Franz Mesmer—from whose name came the expression "to be mesmerized." Though Mesmer achieved credible results with patients having nervous disorders, the medical community scoffed at the idea and both he and his therapy fell into disrepute. Now, however, hypnosis is becoming an important method of therapy in certain instances.

Aside from therapy, altered mental states are now recognized as a normal aspect of life. What we frequently term day-dreaming is nothing more than an altered state of consciousness. Deep thought about a specific problem or situation brings an altered state, and sometimes a brilliant insight. Artists, musicians, and poets work from this level. We all have access to subconscious knowing; Memory calls it forth spontaneously, usually at an opportune time.

Both prayer and meditation produce an altered mental state, often accompanied by a sublime bliss and sense of well-being. Self-healing can occur as a result of guided meditation; prayer is important, it connects one with the cosmic consciousness. Both body and mind respond to these time proven methods of healing and rapture.

The power of Memory and its effect upon mind and body is gaining increased emphasis among psychologists and psychiatrists. They caution the medical profession to be more guarded in their interaction with patients. Memory and consciousness still function even when a person is under anesthesia. We may not have conscious recall of a procedure, but the subconscious hears and remembers. Under hypnosis, former patients have described the details of their operation, including even the conversation of those grouped around the operating table. In many instances, therapists were able to verify a patient's description of the procedure by interviewing those present at the time. Casual comments by a surgeon, such as, "I'd only give this one a 50-50 chance of recovery," may register in the subconscious memory of the patient. This can produce a mental reaction, a subconscious disturbance which retards recuperation and induces a melancholy frame of mind detrimental to normal healing.

Likewise, therapists can sometimes coax memories of birth from adult persons. Chance remarks by a doctor, nurse, or even the mother, can have a lifelong affect on the mental and physical well-being of a person. While under hypnosis, adult persons have described their delivery and any complications which might have arisen, their feelings at the time, and the conversation of those present. Again, many of these accounts received verification after interviewing the mother, the doctor, or both. Mainstream physicians often shun holistic medicine,* but the influence mind exerts over body must be taken into account. Therapists increasingly urge doctors to be more positive in their attitude and remarks, both while giving a prognosis or performing a procedure. Memory, whether it be conscious or subconscious, in an adult or infant, registers regardless of the physical condition of the body and brain at the time an event occurs.

Hypnotic regression back to womb memories? Come now, Dr. Freud's ghost may come back to haunt us for such ideas.

The conventional wisdom up until a couple of

---

*A notable exception is surgeon Bernie S. Siegel. Read his book, *Love, Medicine & Miracles*, 1986, Harper and Row; it may change (or save) your life.

decades back held that newborns reacted from instinct, that perceived smiles were nothing more than muscle spasms or gas pains, that the brain had not developed sufficiently for consciousness to emerge. How then do we account for verifiable memories of abortion attempts made by one's mother, fetal memories of events which happened to a mother while pregnant, or the circumstances accompanying one's conception? Psychological journals carry reports by practicing hypnotherapists describing all these seemingly impossible to remember occurrences.*

If fetal memories are difficult to conceive, consider memories of pastlives that surface during hypnotic regression? Such experiences are not the least uncommon. Dick Sutphen (Note 3 above), though not in medical practice, was an early pioneer in pastlife hypnotic regressions. Dr. Raymond Moody, in *Coming Back* (Note 3, chapter Six), describes the results of his work using hypnotic regressions. Dr. Brian L. Weiss, another practicing psychiatrist, has two books on the same subject: *Many Lives, Many Masters*, 1988, and *Through Time Into Healing*, 1992."[10] Dr. Weiss was astounded when one of his patients began describing a pastlife during hypnosis. Continued hypnotherapy resulted not only in relief of the patient's symptoms, it also provided a sublime illumination directed toward the doctor. Dr. Weiss, at a loss for explanation concerning what had happened, equated the phenomenon with Carl Jung's concept of the Collective Unconscious.

Pastlife experiences suggest that the metaphor concerning silent messengers has a basis of fact in actual practice. Also, experiences of this nature lend

---

*Psychologist David B. Chamberlain has researched and written numerous articles concerning fetal and birth memories. His book, *Babies Remember Birth*, 1989, Tarcher, provides in depth work on the subject.

considerable credence to Rupert Sheldrake's hypothesis of formative causation. His definition of morphic fields also jibes with Jung's concept of the Collective Unconscious.

The phenomenon described by Drs. Moody and Weiss is a common observation reported by many therapists. It's not clear whether such experiences actually represent a pastlife review, or whether they are fabrications of the mind. Some practitioners consider pastlife experiences as valid recall from a previous life, others think they may be a mental aberration resulting from some submerged psychological problem. Whichever, most agree that in some situations pastlife regressions are beneficial forms of therapy.

In some instances, historical research has found that an actual person fitting the pastlife description and circumstances did in fact exist. Many are quick to conclude that such verification constitutes proof of the theory of reincarnation. Also lending support to the theory, such recollections are usually vivid, coherent (as opposed to the symbolism of dreams), and filled with emotion as if they were an actual memory (I know—I've experienced them). However, I have reservations concerning conventional reincarnation theory.

Reincarnation, or Morphic Resonance?

The idea of reincarnation may be among the oldest religious beliefs of mankind, possibly going back to Neanderthal times. But the classic theory of reincarnation has problems. A major snag involves numbers: there wasn't enough people on Earth during previous centuries and millenia for all of us today to have had numerous lifetimes back through history. For instance, the total population of the civilized world at the time when Jesus was born was roughly the same as the present population of the United States. The global population expanded slowly, finally doubling and reaching about one-half billion people by 1650 AD. It doubled again to one billion by 1850. Now, less than 150 years later, Earth's population has increased more than five-fold to approximately 5.5 billion people. At the current rate, world population is doubling about every 40 years or less.

I would venture to guess that an experienced hypnotist could extract at least a half-dozen pastlife memories from 60 to 70% of each of us alive today (I am an amateur hypnotist and can do this well). The arithmetic isn't there. How could most of us today have experienced a lifetime as a priest or priestess serving the temple in ancient Egypt, or lived during the days of the Roman Empire, or have lived in France during the days of the revolution? There just wasn't enough physical bodies to go around for everyone living today. Only one of twenty of us alive today could have been on Earth during the glory days of Egypt, to say nothing of having been a priest or priestess. About the same ratio would hold for the golden era of the Roman Empire. Nearly two thousand years later, only one of seven of us could have lived in the entire world let alone being in France during the revolution. I stick with Isaac Newton, arithmetic supersedes hypnotic recall.

Another criticism concerning conventional reincarnation theory involves an excessive incidence rate of people seeing themselves as a notable historic character: such as seeing themselves as Cleopatra, a famous king, etc. The skeptic is quick to say that such memories are ego related, pure mental fabrications designed to pacify an insecurity or lack of personal esteem. As a friend recently remarked, "Every mental institution in the country has at least one Napoleon." Common sense tells us that only one former Cleopatra or Napoleon could be here at any given time.

But I'm not sure the preceding is a valid criticism. While there are such reports, the majority of pastlife experiences involve very ordinary persons in very ordinary circumstances. I must not have had a glamorous past because I never witnessed myself as being very important to the culture and/or the times. (This also fits with most of those with whom I have compared notes). I did seem drawn toward experiences which coincide with my interests in this lifetime. These explorations helped to explain why I have certain likes and dislikes, why I have certain abilities, why I try to avoid certain situations, why I think as I do. They seem to parallel my present life. At first, this seemed further substantiation of reincarnation, but now I suspect that my subconscious called upon silent messengers to deliver an important lesson. That is, while in an altered state of consciousness, my subconscious scanned the universal data bank for information relevant to today's concerns. Then after selecting a suitable example, silent messengers projected a flash-back of another person's life.

The implications, or lessons, of reincarnation theory remain valid, it's the mechanics involving information dissemination which remain in question. Whether it be Carl Jung's idea of the Collective Unconscious or Sheldrake's morphic resonance, either eliminates the problems associated with conventional reincarnation theory. Both fit into my mythology. The Collective Unconscious and/or morphic fields both describe a spiritual energy field which collects and preserves the life experiences of all those who have ever lived. Then by some unknown process those memories come into consciousness.

Metaphorically speaking, spontaneous visions, hypnosis, or an otherwise induced altered state of consciousness, is akin to changing channels on our mental television set. We then have access to the cosmic consciousness so elegantly described by Richard Bucke. Hundreds of thousands of people can tune into the same consciousness simultaneously without ever having been that actual person. Many of us may subconsciously seek famous persons of history because their experiences in life may be of significance to us in our present life. Memories are not personal, they are not secrets which go to the grave when physical life expires. Memories are shared, handed forward for hundreds and thousands of generations. So, be careful what you think.

My myth does allow reincarnation to happen in a limited number of circumstances. However, it's not a routine occurrence. We investigate possible exceptions in the next two chapters.

Mind

Understanding the functions of Intellect is relatively easy. We don't know how it works, but we use it so frequently that we take it for granted. The roots of Memory are more elusive, more intangible. Mind is unfathomable.

We must not confuse the metaphysical mind with the physical brain. David Chamberlain, previously referenced, writes:

"Neuroscience is not likely to contribute much to psychology, or psychology much to neuroscience, as long as brain continues to be confused with mind. Brain studies do not tell us about extended realms of consciousness."[11]

The brain is no more the seat of the mind than the heart is the source of love and compassion. Such ideas may come from Eastern mythology which identifies seven areas of the body sensitive to spiritual energies. Known as cakras (sometimes spelled chakra), these centers are believed receptors of spiritual energies having various frequency and intensity. The heart cakra receives the energy of transformation, therefore it is associated with love and compassion. The crown cakra (top of the head) receives the energy of transcendence.[12] Though this energy enters at the brain level, the brain does not constitute mind.

Physiologically, the heart is a pump which circulates blood through the body; the brain receives input or stimulus from Mind, then transmits appropriate impulses through the central nervous system. Granted, the brain is a very complex organ, but it facilitates rather than innovates. Both heart and brain are physical systems, sophisticated organs composed of billions of cells. They both decompose after physical death and return to the initial condition—atoms and molecules. Some of that matter may later become the material used to construct the heart of a grizzly bear, the brain of an ant, the branch of a fir tree, or eons into the future—a pebble on some celestial beach.

Mind As A Process

Mind exists in a separate realm completely removed from the physical. It isn't a mechanism like the brain, it is a process, a metaphysical system which thinks, reasons, evaluates and creates. Mind, not neurons, conceives and composes immortal symphonies and creates master works of art. It is a command/control agency which integrates incoming stimulus, then translates and sends appropriate messages to the brain. Sometimes, utilizing Intellect, Mind demands immediate action from the brain. At other times it sends information to Memory for future reference. Mind tells brain what to do, what's important, what's urgent, what's trivial. Brain, being physical, then tells the physical body how to behave, how to act and react. Mind is the totality of mental function, it can override the decisions of Intellect, it has access to Memory beyond present life experiences.

The metaphysical Mind receives information sent by silent messengers, a process which metaphorically works something like television. All knowledge, ideas, thoughts, and historical events reside as Memory in the universal data bank. The UDB is a field of spiritual energy which exists throughout the Universe. Unlike earthly transmissions, these are broadcast over an infinite number of channels (unlimited amplitude and frequency). Mind is the receiver set, or more specifically, a relay station which intercepts messages from any number of sources. It then evaluates and translates incoming information, makes an appropriate decision, and issues a command to the brain. The brain and central nervous system, though they be physical, are elaborate organs capable of converting commands of Mind into bodily action. Like television, mind has volume control, a channel selector, brightness controls, and antenna. And like earthly programming, some channels are enlightening and inspirational, others are trite and depressing. The secret to happiness and a full life is knowing when to change channels.

Whether the chain of communication originates

in spirit or results from sensual stimulus, Mind receives the impulse and instantly invokes Intellect and Memory to assist in evaluating the input. It then sends instructions to the brain. Brain is the physical component which completes the circuit.

Being a physical organ, the brain is vulnerable to injury and disease. Injury to the brain can block Memory from what we might call ordinary consciousness, impair functions of the Intellect, or completely separate Mind from the temporal body as when in a comatose state. Brain injuries are analogous to a burnt out transistor in a television set: the picture goes blank even though the transmission is uninterrupted. It's the receiver which doesn't work. Brain, the receiver, never gets the message and the body does not respond, but consciousness still exists (NDEs for example).

Mind is therefore a complicated process which employs an amalgamation of thoughts, ideas, mental states, and levels of awareness. It is a metaphysical process, a thinking and creating innovator. Stated in computer jargon, Mind is nonphysical software which programs the physical hardware known as brain. Intellect resembles the operating system, Memory the data base. The result of this process produces an overt act performed by a physical body. Mind must always select from a wide variety of options. It can direct a physical body to create a master work of art, or it could plot a murder or plan a bank robbery.

Mind As A System Far-From-Equilibrium

Why do some people write books while others initiate wars? It depends upon how Mind processes information and selects various choices. Intellect is to some extent molded to conform with the social standards and intellectual environment of a given society. Since Intellect normally influences functions of Mind, certain attitudes and morals become established early in life as a result of parental training and by the social and political atmosphere in a community, a state, a nation. People in the United States have a distinctive mind-set, the people of India have another. Because of our conditioned programming, the people of the United States are more prone to go to war than the people of India. In the United States, conflict is a viable choice for resolving disputes, those in India might choose a more passive method.

But generalized observations ignore individual behavior because the human mind is considerably more complex than mere conformity to a collective mind-set. It is completely unpredictable as attested to by the news each day. Mind can rise to high summits of excellence, it can also descend into the depths of barbaric behavior. Fluctuating emotions can result in macroscopic mood swings and inconsistent behavior, either for good or for bad.

This unpredictability of mind function seems to conform to an as yet relatively new concept of physics. Frequently going under the heading of chaos, it is more properly identified as nonlinear dynamical systems. It is an exciting new field which attracts scientists from all disciplines; it's also in its infancy and the mathematics for practical application are burdensome.

We won't get bogged down trying to explain nonlinear dynamical systems except to note that they are open systems which remain dynamical, not reaching a conclusive end-point (equilibrium, or steady state).[13] These systems are repetitive with output from a previous cycle automatically feeding back into the dynamics driving the system. Feedback remains in the system which accumulates and effects each successive iteration (repeat of the process). Such a system has sensitive dependence to the initial condition, meaning that any error or mistake in establishing the initial parameters becomes magnified during each iteration. Eventually these perturbations (disturbances) will gain so much magnitude that the system may self-destruct: chaos being the final result.

An example of nonlinear dynamics would be a column of soldiers marching across a bridge structurally designed to support ten times their combined weight. If they fall out of step they have a safe crossing. However, if they remain in step their combined tromp-tromp-tromp may generate vibrations in the bridge structure. Nonlinear dynamics take over when each vibration feeds back adding more energy to the system, this in turn causing ever more violent vibrations. If the column of soldiers is long enough, at some point the bridge may shake itself apart—its collapse being a state of chaos for both the structure and those soldiers unlucky enough to have been on the bridge.

Not all nonlinear dynamical systems proceed to chaos. Sometimes a higher state of order emerges. Consider learning for instance.[14] Intellect receives incoming information, subjects it to analysis, classifies it according to its importance, then sends it to the appropriate file in Memory. But Memory contributes to information analysis by feeding back to Intellect previously attained knowledge pertinent to the incoming information. The feedback loop is continuous and each cycle refines, clarifies, and adds to the original input. This exchange increases the energy available for thinking, creativity, and objective analysis. With unrestricted feedback, the learning process accelerates. Mental functions remain a dynamical system ever evolving toward a higher state of order. (But this higher order isn't always what society wants—it also applies to planning bank robberies and military invasions).

In some instances mental feedback can be detrimental. If Mind becomes opinionated, set and rigid in its thinking, the feedback loop slips into a rut and cycles the same information over and over. When this happens, learning ceases and mental functions reach equilibrium (no longer dynamic). Consciousness becomes stable, doomed to the status quo.

The learning process can suffer other pitfalls. Since nonlinear dynamical systems are extremely sensitive to the initial condition, errors and other perturbations can significantly restrict learning. As an example, getting the hang of calculus presented a problem for me in the early going. Somehow, I had acquired some erroneous perceptions, or faulty assumptions. These misconceptions fed back to perturb my comprehension of successive phases. Each mistake led to more mistakes. Chaos reigned. Then one day while contemplating a practical problem in physics, the entire idea behind calculus suddenly flooded into my mind (an intuitive insight, discussed in the next section). I then understood that anything involving variable rate of change required calculus for solution. Once I understood the fundamentals, my problems ceased. Order out of chaos.[15]

It is becoming increasingly apparent that nonlinear dynamics enter into virtually all complex systems one way or another: systems such as biological evolution, the history of civilizations, social trends, economic cycles, politics, medicine, climatology, seismology, and on and on. Any repetitive system which is sensitive to the initial condition is subject to possible chaos after a large number of iterations. A minor error or disturbance at the beginning may eventually cause self-destruction of the system. (One rotten apple spoils the entire barrel—a problem inherent within American politics today).

The mechanics involving biological evolution are clearly driven by nonlinear dynamics. In Chapter Two we noticed that biological progress accelerated exponentially; that is, new and advanced species arrived after ever shorter time intervals. And, advancement usually emerged from chaotic conditions (following a period of mass extinction). Then after coming into being, a species or an entire ecosystem slid along relatively unchanged for a long time. During its existence, invisible feedback loops from past generations passed forward to future generations. Even a slight deformity at the beginning would amplify until suddenly, without archaeological warning, a species succumbed to extinction.* Then along came another more advanced species to take its place. Feedback through many generations (iterations) led to chaos for one species, it handed forward the genetic information (or morphic resonance) essential to advancing life forms. Species came and went, but each successive species was superior to the one preceding it. Again, order emerges from chaos. Not many microbiologists overtly embrace this idea, a few skirt around the possibility. I think it probable that as nonlinear dynamical systems become better understood, neo-Darwinism will drift into the backwaters of archaic biology.

At first I was somewhat disappointed with Rupert Sheldrake because I felt that he went to the brink of suggesting that evolution was driven by nonlinear dynamical systems, then backed off before taking the

---

*Drastic changes in the environment (an unexpected perturbation coming from within the ecosystem), coupled with an inability to adapt, would be chaotic for many species.

plunge. However, his reluctance is well explained in a later book.* I'm now content to let him paddle his canoe in familiar waters. Nonetheless, his ideas are certainly consistent with nonlinear dynamics (in my opinion, morphic resonance is virtually synonymous with feedback during many iterations).

Back to the mind and the implications of nonlinear dynamics.

Suppose that an individual receives an overdose of data input, sensual or otherwise. It swirls around in consciousness as Intellect tries to interpret its meaning, significance, or consequences. Memory has no recall of any such previous experience. Mixed and confusing signals go to the Mind. Mind wrestles with a tangle of seemingly unrelated thoughts, sensations, and emotions. Indecision, frustration, uncertainty, and a complete lapse of mental facilities may follow. Dependent upon the severity of the overload, a good night's sleep or a long walk may allow Mind to clear itself. Or, failing this, one might fall into a state of deep depression which could eventually require professional therapy.

Another person might grapple with mental confusion or emotional instability, sort through the thoughts, rearrange the input, and then recognize a correlation between thoughts—a pattern emerges. From the initial disorder might burst a brilliant insight. It's been said that genius and insanity are separated by a narrow corridor. A micro-shift one way or the other might determine whether one finds a cure for cancer or ends up in a straight jacket.

---

*Trialogues At The Edge Of The West: Chaos, Creativity, and the Resacralization of the World, by Ralph Abraham, Terence McKenna, and Rupert Sheldrake, 1992, Bear & Co.

SPIRITUAL AWARENESS

Does the conscious mind of itself constitute the totality of consciousness? I don't think so. It comes close but something is still missing. One other ingredient is essential to extended human consciousness.

Mind itself knows that it knows, it knows what it knows, it knows how to use what it knows. But without Spiritual Awareness, Mind labors in a partial vacuum. Only that knowledge acquired by sensual input and accumulated learning enter the Intellect, and therefore, Memory. One could, and many do, go through life acting out the drama of day-to-day affairs with nothing more than Mind. Mind itself could analyze life situations, it could plan for the future, it could engage in intellectual debate, it could carry one to high social status, it could take one to the moon and back. Such a life would be somewhat robotic, programmed in large part by others, structured to fit socially imposed expectations, a kind of come as it may, go with the flow existence. Such would be life if one never tuned into the higher spiritual energies.

Extended consciousness is what separates man from the remainder of the animal kingdom (is my species chauvinism showing?). It comes from an inner urge, an undefinable yearning to be more than what we outwardly display on the surface of life. Extended consciousness is what prompts us to write symphonies, to create master works of art, to demonstrate compassion, to love, to recognize the existence of a higher Being. Extended consciousness is the trait of humanity that allows us to express the subjectivity contained within the inner-self; it is the component of Being that hears and obeys the voice of angels.

Some say that extended consciousness wells up

from that little understood thing termed the subconscious mind. Like other mind functions, we don't know for sure what the subconscious is, or how it works. Some think the subconscious resides in the right hemisphere of the brain; however, since I've removed mind/consciousness from brain, my myth would say that the subconscious is a delicate receiver which tunes into the wisdom conveyed by silent messengers (perhaps the translation occurs in the right hemisphere). Extended consciousness tells us things we don't know that we know, it calls forth memories of events and experiences from another time and place beyond our earthly adventure. It is the human ingredient of Being, that special attribute unique to only one species. It receives nourishment from the highest of all spiritual energies—Spiritual Awareness.

Intuition

Intuition is a subjective way of knowing unlike Intellect which requires conscious cognition. Intuitive knowing is effortless. It often requires proper mental conditioning such as a calm mood or entering an altered state of consciousness. Altered states (such as prayer, hypnosis, meditation, dreams, or times of extreme mental or physical duress as with a NDE) still the conscious mind which allows the subconscious to bring its knowing into intellectual perception.

Intuitive knowing can take several forms. The most frequent may be the gut-feeling, a hunch, a conviction which defies logic and reason. Hunches are subtle and if one shrugs off such a feeling it flitters away, gone and lost. At other times Intuition comes spontaneously, a sudden flash of knowing as if from blue sky. Spontaneous reception usually involves an insight, an idea, a solution to a problem, an inspiration.

Induced Intuitive knowing such as viewing other-pastlives while hypnotized comes in visual form, with sound or its equivalent, sometimes incorporating other people and strange geographic settings. Intuitive knowing draws from an eternal data bank immeasurably large compared to that generated by the Intellect and sent to Memory in the conscious Mind. It draws from a field of memory which encompasses the history of the Universe. Its power is awesome; its energy forms the fundamental footing of Spiritual Awareness.

The Subconscious Mind

The conscious and subconscious minds represent a duality in mental systems. That is, conscious knowing is a learning process, subconscious knowing (Intuition) is a gift bestowed by the Universe. Conscious knowing is what leads us through physical life, subconscious knowing reminds us that life is more than mere working, eating, and making love. The two ways of knowing bring the psyche into balance. The gift of the subconscious is creativity and spiritual awareness, conscious knowing supports the physical aspect of Being. The two, working in unison, comprise that mysterious quality we call extended consciousness.

Don't confuse Intuition with Instinct. Intuition is a mental process, an unconscious way of knowing. Instincts, discussed earlier, are involuntary reactions resulting in a physical response to external stimuli or internal feelings. We instinctively pull our hand back when we accidentally touch a hot object, we instinctively become cautious when approaching the brink of a high cliff, we instinctively run from a dangerous situation. Procreation is an instinct consummated by a physical act. Instincts are nature's way of protecting its creatures, an involuntary way of avoiding the hazards of life.

Intuition is nature's way of informing its creatures of future conditions, of providing information vital to growth and advancement. Intuition is a higher order of spiritual energy than is instinctive reaction. It is what told the robins and geese that it was safe to return early, it tells animals about impending disasters, it guides them across unfamiliar terrain, it is a benevolent counselor to all creatures. Intuition is the portal through which silent messengers enter consciousness.

The conscious component of Mind tends to be rather arrogant and domineering, somewhat like a Missouri mule—stubborn and not believing anything until shown. It is proud of Intellect, it boasts its ability to reason, and given its own way it would rely completely upon logic. It too often ignores the subconscious, sometimes to the extent that it denies the existence of any other mental facility other than its own powers.

The subconscious mind is clever. It recognizes the subservient role imposed by the conscious mind upon its intuitive powers. But it has its say; it influences the conscious mind in subtle ways.

The subconscious is the root of creativity, of emotion, of compassion, of love, of inspiration and devotion. It sends subliminal messages to the body which affects our attitudes, which sometimes causes an inexplicable yearning. Intuition influences our mental and physical health, it is the architect of subjective endeavors, it kindles ideas, it furnishes information inaccessible to the conscious mind. The subconscious sneaks into prominence whenever the conscious mind drops its guard—such as rendering a hunch, a spontaneous insight, or when one deliberately enters an altered state of consciousness. The subconscious, more than the conscious mind, constitutes the wholeness of Being. We ought to give it more credence, to trust its benevolent guidance.

The Portal To Extended Consciousness

Trust is the prop which holds open the door to Intuition. We too often receive an insight, then the conscious mind, jealous of its ability to analyze and interpret incoming information, rationalizes us into discounting Intuition. "This is not in my experience," says the conscious mind, "pay it no attention." So we drop the idea or fresh viewpoint which has mysteriously popped into the mind. And by so doing, we deprive ourselves of information which might enrich our lives. Our silent messengers probably shake their heads in frustration.

On the other hand, if we command the conscious mind to back-off and then experiment with Intuition, we will soon recognize its reliability. Listening to Intuition and applying it to practical situations fortify trust. Repeated success through following Intuition will soon force the conscious mind to become more tolerant. In time the two ways of knowing will merge into one integrated thinking and learning system—one then achieves extended consciousness. Spirit enters physical life and the world takes on new luster.

Establishing this contact with Spirit requires practice as well as trust. The more we listen to Spirit, the more we hear, the more we see, the better we feel. We should take some time out of each day to listen, to be still and know. This means interrupting the busy and hurried lifestyle which captivates modern societies.

We should reserve a minimum of one hour a day for personal reflection, introspection, meditation, or prayer—60 minutes to still the conscious mind and escape from mundane concerns. It should become a part of family life, an hour for mom, for dad, yes even for each of the youngsters. There would be far less physical ailments, fewer mental and emotional disturbances, enhanced learning at school, more peace and harmony in the home. And don't say you don't have time. Most of our running through life is a form of escape, an addiction to materialism, a denial of Spirit.

Be still and know. Jesus spoke of this, he also counseled quiet prayer in a private place (in your closet if nowhere else). The Buddha received enlightenment while meditating beneath the bo-tree. Mohammed received the fundamentals of Islam during a long series of revelations received while secluded in deep meditation. Trusting Intuition and putting it into practice is an old idea, but it has fallen into a subservient role in human cognition. As consciousness expanded, a long contest ensued between Intellect and Intuition. Intellect gradually gained ground and it now holds a substantial lead. If the trend continues, mankind loses.

How can we reverse the trend? We've already answered the question. Be still and know. Trust what you receive. Put your intuitive powers to work, demand that the intellectual mind cooperate with the subjective mind. Both ways of knowing are essential to extended consciousness.

Order, Or Chaos?

Extended consciousness expands as one comes to trust Intuition. It seems to operate something like a physical nonlinear dynamical system. Loops of intuitive feedback cycle through consciousness providing an influx of new knowledge and information. This results in an elevated state of awareness, each level above the preceding one. Positive intuitive feedback from Spiritual Awareness eventually penetrates society at large (a field of collective sentiment). It gains in volume and strength until finally global attitudes escalate resulting in extended consciousness throughout the nations of the world. World peace, ecological harmony, the defeat of crime and warfare will come from the intuitive energy field of Spiritual Awareness.

In contrast, negativity feeds upon negativity (the current mode as exemplified by present global politics). If the majority of world thinking continues to center around economics, materialism, egotism, and apathy toward nature, the system will at some point collapse into a state of chaos. Chaos in this instance would be rampant fear and anxiety, increased conflict, and continued deterioration of Earth's environment.

We have a choice, it can go either way. History has shown time and again that a minority brought about all positive or negative social changes. Ten to twenty percent of any given population can lead an apathetic majority in either direction. Though it be a matter of perception, consider the American Revolution in contrast to the Bolshevik Revolution. Why not reach for positive change which leads to extended consciousness? If we eliminate the negative, positive mental feedback loops would gain intensity during each cycle adding increased energy to the social system. Eventually a lethargic system would jump from near equilibrium conditions (the status quo) into a higher and more positive state of order.

Therefore, when enough people (10 to 20%) think peace, become genuinely concerned about the environment, turn away from exclusive pursuit of self-interests, their positive mental feedback enters Earth's spiritual aura. The aura glows, the dark shadows of negativity dissipate. Its radiance will sway public attitudes, Earth will be a better place to live.

Yes, I know that some people will say this can never happen. Man is inherently aggressive, the most indiscriminate predator to walk the face of Mother Earth. Man can't and won't change because that's not his nature.

You've heard the argument. It has an element of truth because Western Society has suffered three or more millenia of negative feedback. Our collective consciousness is at the edge of chaos, but is reversible. If a few more of us think *positive*, the power of Spirit will lift Society to higher states of order.

Wonderment

Wonderment isn't a thing learned, it isn't any special knowledge or information, it isn't an unusual ability, it isn't a state of mind. Wonderment is an experience. Or more to the point, it is experienc*ing*. It is mobile, enthusiastic, an ever growing sense of joy and contentment. It blooms after the seeds of Intuition germinate. It has no bounds, it ever expands to encompass the essence of Being.

Wonderment is an awareness of the spiritual link which connects all of nature with Unity. The connection is all inclusive, a mutual bond not only with the Source, but also including other creatures. Spirit does not differentiate between its creatures nor assign orders of importance to the millions of species who claim Mother Earth as their home. All creatures have a purpose, all perform a service, all are essential to the perpetuation of life on the planet. The Creator harbors and protects a buttercup with the same loving care and diligence as it does for humans. We are all a part of the One, and without the collective total of all life, the Creator itself would be incomplete.

I think Jesus was trying to convey this idea when he said, "Blessed are the meek: for they shall inherit the earth." Meek in this sense doesn't mean being timid, shy, or reclusive. It means the acceptance of Spirit, the recognition of nature as a reflection of a kind and gentle Creator. It means appreciation of what is, what will always be.

Enlightenment

I don't have much to say about Enlightenment, I'm not there. In fact, I'm not sure about being comfortably settled into Wonderment—I'm still grappling with the Intuition thing. The most I can do is guess about the Enlightenment.

Perhaps it is a transcendental state of awareness, the highest form of spiritual energy to enter Earth's aura. For some reason it seems to elude most of us. I do sense the wonders of the Universe, the beauty of nature, the grandeur of Spirit. But sensing is not experiencing.

Maybe Enlightenment represents a mental union with the Source, for consciousness to be consumed by Unity. It could be a blissful state where all life forms are seen as indistinguishable parts of the One. It might be tuning into the energy field of infinite love, a state where hate, greed, envy, and lust disappear as a fog burns off under the morning sun.

Probably not many of us achieve this state while in the physical. We have a strong attachment to Mother

Earth, the strings are hard to break. Enlightenment probably involves some personal sacrifices, a giving up of something to gain another. The Buddha forsake earthly attachments to achieve the Enlightenment. Jesus disdained all earthly pleasures. History is resplendent with martyrs, people who gave their all for the sake of a conviction, a knowing, a divine principle.

Maybe it isn't intended that all of us reach the Enlightenment while in the physical. We came into the physical for a reason, to serve a purpose, to learn something which only the High One knows. Maybe we must pass back into Spirit to know the answers, to attain the Enlightenment. If so, we have something to look forward to.

Despite its unfathomable characteristics, Spiritual Awareness with its three levels of energy beams downward to activate all other life forces. It guides human activities, it shapes our attitudes, it illuminates our knowing. It is the summit of Being. At this level exclusiveness yields to Unity, one experiences joy through interconnectedness with all of Nature.

> *When you begin to think you have achieved spirituality, you probably haven't. When you begin experiencing the spiritual, you are.*

Chapter Eight

THE MYTH

Back To The Initial Condition, And Afterward

Without implying an absence of subjectivity, we note that Stephen Hawking's concept of black holes and proposed no boundary model of the Universe both rely upon mathematics for derivation. The majority of us couldn't begin to understand the methodology and reasoning behind Hawking's work. But, lest we discount the validity of his conclusions, consider that most known mechanisms of nature (physics) conform to mathematical description. It's not as if Isaac Newton invented calculus, he discovered a language which describes the physical Universe.* So, even though few of us comprehend higher mathematics, we must acknowledge that its equations accurately define most physical systems (thanks to Super-consciousness). Mathematics, by its inherent nature, is subjective even for those who work with it on a daily basis.

Black Elk's tepee rings are without doubt subjective. They are symbolic of the workings of nature as

---

*Not all mathematicians would agree with this statement. Some think that the creative mind of man invented mathematics as a language to define physical systems. Others think that math pre-existed human consciousness. My view follows the latter, again paralleling the Anthropic Principle.

observed by many generations of people whose very existence depended upon the provisions given by Mother Earth. Those of us without a background in math can better understand Black Elk because we can also feel the swirl of the wind, observe the change of seasons, see the wheel of life which begins with infancy and ends with infancy. We relate to Black Elk because anyone with eyes to see, ears to hear, and a thinking mind can duplicate his conclusions.

Considering the disparity between methods, it is indeed more than coincidence that both models lead to a similar concept—recurring cycles returning to the initial condition before repeating. Hawking applied his mathematics to the grand scale of the Universe, Black Elk observed the microscopic elements which exist in one tiny corner of the Universe. The principle holds true regardless of size and scale. In either case, both Hawking's and Black Elk's concepts relate to the physical Universe. They deal with the tangible, the temporal, the observable.

Again, assuming symmetry between the physical and the metaphysical, we might expect that the cycles of nature come forward from a pre-existing principle established long ago by the Mind of the Creator. Since we don't know His/Her Mind, we will employ the cycles of nature as a model to construct a myth describing the metaphysical aspect of Being.

The Mystery Of Death

Most surviving myths contain a provision for origins, as did the early chapters of this book. But before the human mind grappled with origins, it probably contemplated and worried about the mystery of death. How can you understand a cold stiff body which yesterday walked and laughed and brought joy to others? Is life futile and senseless, or is a higher purpose hidden from consciousness?

Concern with the hereafter troubled the mind of very primitive people. It is apparent that Neanderthal man was conscious of a higher order in life. Numerous Neanderthal grave sites have been excavated, some dating back 70 to 75 thousand years. These sites suggest an elaborate burial ceremony during which the grave was furnished with food, clothing, tools, and items for personal adornment. We have no way of knowing what these ancient people believed, but quoting Mircea Eliade,[1] "...the presence of such objects implies not only belief in a personal survival but also the certainty that the deceased will continue his particular activity in the other world." If Eliade's explanation is correct (nobody has come up with a better idea), metaphysical concepts arrived on the planet concurrent with, or possibly before, the appearance of modern man.

Whichever, consciousness had a long time to stew and ponder the mystery of life and death. Over time stories developed, legends were born, ceremonials celebrated the milestones of life, symbols became a way to illustrate that which was otherwise unexplainable. Metaphysical concepts became a myth for a given culture. And from mythology sprang the religions of the world.

What prompted Neanderthal man to think about life in the hereafter? The atheist might say that once man became aware of his impending death, his fear of the unknown demanded an escape route. Life after death?—pure fantasy, a denial of the inevitable, nothing but wishful thinking.

This brushoff may satisfy the mind of some, but it

is indeed strange that thousands of generations in widely divergent cultures arrived at approximately the same ideas concerning life and death. Granted, the various customs and rituals cover a broad spectrum of beliefs and traditional ceremonies, but the underlying belief is similar—crossing over into paradise, or, eternal existence in Spirit when earthly life expires. Though countless gods and goddesses parade through the beliefs of man, a belief in the afterlife has carried forward for millenia after millenia with little change in theme.

But this is history, it doesn't answer the question as to why Neanderthal contemplated an existence in the hereafter. The answer reverts to metaphysical concepts, it involves a mysterious way of knowing (Intuition). Primitive religions refer to the "voice of Spirit", a communication received by a shaman or wise elder of the tribe. Later religions had prophets who received certain knowledge during prayer or meditation. Perhaps more influential, man seems imbued with a residual yearning for the sublime.

This myth employs silent messengers who transmit information from Spirit into the physical. This knowledge comes from a field of infinite love, hope, and inspiration. This knowing is accessible to all who trust Intuition. The myth also recognizes that modern man still longs for an affiliation with his Creator.

The details of a particular myth are not particularly important, it's mostly a matter of which myth feels right. Though each historic tradition claims to have found the only true way, they all say about the same thing if stripped to bare basics. This continuity through eons of time bespeaks a consistent and ever present source of knowledge. For lack of better terms, I'll simply say that Intuition receives and deciphers all cosmic knowledge disseminated by silent messengers.

Now, to answer my question, I'd have to say that Neanderthal listened to the voice of Spirit and by so knowing he perceived the continuity of life beyond earthly existence.

Nature, Soul, and Spirit

It's easy to speak of Spirit, to comprehend Spirit is another matter. Ask any ten people for a definition and you will get five blank stares and five different opinions. Or, ask another ten to differentiate between *spirit* and *soul.* Most will shrug and say they mean the same thing.

Since we are dealing with metaphysical concepts, it isn't surprising that many different ideas evolved through countless centuries of emerging culture. We previously noted that Western Society shifted its attention toward the soul, particularly its salvation. Our orthodoxy became predominantly exclusive in that it prescribes salvation in intricate detail, it is quite specific regarding the consequences which befall those who stray from *the way.* Only lately did spirituality creep into Western consciousness, and since our philosophy and theology are essentially devoid of spiritual concepts, we must resort to our own devices to decipher its meaning.

Now I don't wish to become embroiled in a theological debate concerning the distinction between soul and Spirit. I can't give an adequate description of either, nor can anybody else. Nevertheless, we speak of soul in a rather casual manner, as if only a moron didn't know its essence. We flounder about in uncertainty when it comes to Spirit. We do sense that Spirit is mystic, something elusive, something we can experience but never know.

This spiritual void causes a deficiency in awareness. We need to bring spirituality into the forefront of consciousness. Therefore, this myth requires a definition of soul and Spirit, and a differentiation between the two. It's not my intent to assemble a body of converts, or persuade anybody to accept my way of thinking. But as a basis for discussion, consider the following distinctions:

Soul has identity, an essence unique to every person. It is the immortal part of being, that which transcends physical death, the I Am, the personal ego. The soul might be the conscience which fashions our morals and values, our Intuition which distinguishes right from wrong, a guide which leads us through life and into the hereafter. The soul might be the major component of that elusive thing we call Mind. Soul is the immortal part of Being, something we all have, something from which we can never escape.

Spirit, on the other hand seems universal, accessible to all, yet monopolized by none. Spirit is a form of energy, a substance upon which the soul feeds, an omnipresence which permeates all things through all time. Spirit is compassion and love, knowledge and wisdom; it is a subtle influence which directs, motivates, and inspires all life forms. Spirit is a higher energy than that of the soul. It is inclusive, a connective agency which bonds all things to each other and to the Source.

Since Spirit is sublime and elusive, its force field cannot be taken to the laboratory for analysis (yet?). The most we can do is eavesdrop on Spirit through observing nature. We might detect Spirit in the breath of a cool evening breeze, watch its fingers rustle the tree tops, hear its voice in the gurgle of a stream, sense its joy as expressed in the cry of the newborn. We may feel its radiance and become comfortable in the recognition that Spirit protects and preserves all life. Perhaps we could say that Spirit embodies all of nature. Or said another way, nature is the physical manifestation of Spirit.

Physical nature and Spirit are therefore intimates although they exist in different dimensions. Each depends upon the other, one exists in a vacuum without the other. They are mutually attractive, each being a reflection of the other.

Natural Dualities

Any myth worth living must bring both nature and Spirit into equal consideration. It should also incorporate individual souls. We must also account for one other phenomenon which exists throughout the physical Universe, throughout mythology, throughout folklore. This last consideration involves the pairing of opposites, the dualities which bring a system into balance or equilibrium.

The pairing of opposites is woven into most classic legends. An ever popular theme involves bringing heroes and villains into conflict: David slays the giant Goliath, the good guy Robin Hood steals from the rich and gives to the poor, the charming prince kills the dragon to rescue the beautiful princess. The same theme provides the framework for most modern novels and movie scripts. Governments exploit the good guy versus the bad guy syndrome to generate patriotic hysteria among its citizens thereby enticing them to attack and destroy their neighbors.

We see duality throughout physical systems, throughout human nature. Within human thought systems, this pairing of opposites, or conflict between extremes, underlies the cultural traditions of all societies. Duality is central to ancient fables and mythology, poets and prophets brought it into their work, it has remained at the core of modern religions. Used in this context, duality expresses righteousness opposing evil, empathy-apathy, compassion-indifference, saint-demagogue, love-hate, male-female, life-death, heaven-hell, God-Satan, and on and on. Much of our thinking and many emotions are formulated, and sometimes manipulated, according to the principle of duality.

Most of observed duality is concrete, some is merely a matter of perception. The bad guys may perceive themselves the good guys, the enemy is the hero in his homeland, righteousness may also be seen as evil from another's perspective. Perceptions are relative and therefore deceiving—they provide good copy for journalists, allow unscrupulous evangelists to steal from the faithful, inspire action-packed movies, and tend to splinter societies both at the community level and on the global spectrum. Such dual perceptions induce prejudice and alienation, but we won't dwell on them because they are states of mind; instead, we will focus on philosophical and physical dualities.

Physical Duality

Isaac Newton formally reduced physical duality to mathematical form when he derived the equations for his Second Law of Motion (every action has an equal and opposite reaction). This resulted in duality becoming a fundamental concept of physics. Thus began a long sequence of discoveries involving dualities in physical systems.

A bar magnet is a simple example of physical duality. As young students we watched in fascination as a field of force arranged and rearranged metallic particles on a sheet of paper overlaying a magnet. We could actually see the otherwise invisible magnetic field. We learned that a magnet has two poles—north and south. We also learned that opposite poles attract, that like poles repel each other. The metal filings on the paper showed that the forces were neutral at the middle of the bar.

Nature doesn't like lonesome polarities, she likes them in opposing pairs. If poles become separated, nature balances the system by creating an opposite polarity. For example, if we saw through a bar magnet at the middle, we don't end up with a north pole on one piece and a south pole on the other. Instead, the piece originally having the north pole will instantly create a south pole of the end just separated. Likewise, a north pole will appear at the cut on the piece originally having the south pole.

Nature forbids a naked polarity (an absence of duality). All systems must have an equal and opposite component. And it must be opposite otherwise the system would not be neutral, or balanced. Like polarities repeal each other and therefore cannot coexist.

Electric charges have dual components, the positive and the negative. Again, like charges repel, opposites attract. The positive and negative charges live in close association and collectively bring the system into a state of neutrality. The carbon atom, an essential element to all biological life, will serve to illustrate another example of how nature brings a system into balance (a state of stability). The nucleus of the carbon atom contains 12 neutrons having zero electric charge and 12 protons having a positive charge.[2] To be stable, an atom must have neutral charge. Therefore, 12 electrons having a negative charge orbit the nucleus in proximity to the protons. The net electrical charge is neutral, the atom is stable.

In particle physics, science postulates that for every particle of matter there exists a near equal part of antimatter; supersymmetry presumes that for every particle there is a virtual partner having reverse but similar characteristics. Any closed system which returns to the initial condition has equal and opposite components: an expanding and contracting universe, life/death in biological systems, daylight and darkness, summer and winter.

We sometimes don't see the universality of duality because of time restraints. This is because we don't observe the complete cycle, we only experience a small segment in many cases. Right now we see an expanding universe. The contraction, either according to Big Bang theory or Hawking's no boundary model, lies in the future. The cycle is not complete. Here on Earth, we see advancing biological evolution, we can't see devolution which will occur as the Sun burns out and expands.

Our situation parallels that of a mosquito whose life span lasts only a few days. It comes into being during warm summer evenings. If asked to characterize life on Earth, the mosquito would boldly state that the environment is always warm and damp. They don't experience the full seasonal cycle, but we who do can predict with confidence that fall and winter will inevitably follow summer.

Philosophical Duality

Science didn't discover the duality principle; Newton merely reduced it to analytical form. It's an old idea, going back at least as far as ancient China. Their folklore contains an excellent concept of duality, together with a symbolic method of bringing opposing pairs into balance.

The Chinese concept of duality became known as yin-yang. Its symbol is shown by Fig. 8-1

Fig. 8-1
The Tao of All That Is

The yang is the light, the masculine, the active, the forceful. In modern terminology it might describe aggression, competition, logic, the material. It is the manifest. Yin is the dark, the feminine, the mysterious, the sublime, the passive, the docile. Today we may think of it as peace, cooperation, subjectivity, the concealed.

Both the yin and yang lay within a circle which represents a marriage, or union, of the two to form the whole. The twisted "S" shaped boundary between the two represents a close interlocking of both characteristics (the boundary connects two offset semi-circles). Laying in intertwined proximity, the symbol depicts opposite attributes, each signifying the incompleteness of one without the other. The two small dots of opposite shades indicate each having a trace of the other; that is, the yang possesses a touch of yin, the yin has a trace of yang.

Yin and yang are counterparts of the One. They lay close together, they exchange attributes, one cannot exist without the other. Neither is good or bad, they are merely reflections of one another, two opposing parts comprising the whole.

The yin and yang, laying in close association within a bounded confinement, interacting and comprising the whole, express the ultimate concept of balance and harmony. When considered as a totality, they represent neutrality, a balance of energies. Snuggled together in their small nest, they form *Unity*.

Unity, a composite of opposites, best describes the whole of Being, it containing both the physical and spiritual. The physical is a reflection, or a virtual partner of Spirit. We might view the yang as being the physical, the yin being the spiritual aspect of Being. Yang is the active Universe, expanding, dynamic. Yang is the Earth, evolving, swarming with millions of life forms, a subsystem harboring millions of smaller and inconspicuous subsystems. Yin, the spiritual, is passive, elusive, subjective, concealed. Yin, carried by silent messengers, contains the cosmic blueprint, the instructions for physical and biological systems, the ultimate reality hidden in Unity. The physical and the spiritual, when combined and functioning in unison, produce perfect balance, complete neutrality, Unity is at the core of all that is.

A Universe composed of two distinctly opposite yet inextricable components, separated by a barrier, interacting and cooperating, combined to form the One— how do we reconcile this idea in the mind's eye?

Dual Universe

Myths need a symbol, a visual reference to explain that which remains unknowable. Black Elk's circle is a starting point; it incorporates the symbolism of yin-

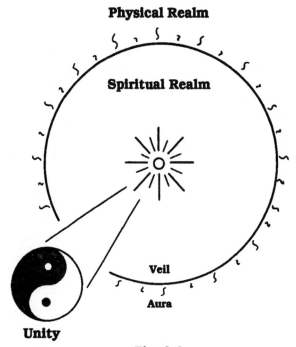

Fig. 8-2
The Dual Universe

yang, it adheres to our graphic description of a closed system.

Fig. 8-2 forms the basic structure of our symbol, we will add details as the myth unfolds.

At the center of our symbol lays Unity, the Source of all that is. It represents the Mind, Intent, and Purpose of the Creator. Unity is neither male nor female, good or bad, saintly or corrupt. It just is. It contains infinite spiritual energy, its diverse force fields yield neutrality, it represents complete balance and perfect symmetry.

The Inner Universe—The Spiritual

The area inside the outer circle represents the Spiritual Realm. Wisdom illuminates this region, love and compassion energize it. Time does not exist, matter is absent. There is neither pain nor sorrow, only peace and contentment. The area outside the larger circle represents the physical realm. Here dualities prevail, matter comes into being, time marches forward, biological systems flourish.

A veil surrounds the periphery of the Spiritual Realm which prohibits those in the physical from peeking into Spirit. They have access to information disseminated by silent messengers, but otherwise they can only feel and sense the power and wonder which resides within Spirit. Intuition provides the awe felt by those in the physical.

While still in Spirit, tiny particles of energy containing the life essence radiate outward from Unity. These small particles of life-force congregate near the veil awaiting an opportunity to cross-over into the physical. During this outward migration, different particles of the life-force receive different instructions concerning their physical sojourn. Some are destined to become a giant redwood tree, some a small sprig of grass, others will become animate creatures. With humans, by the time the life essence reaches the veil it has become what we call the soul.* Soul hovers near the veil, then at the appropriate time, a portion of its energy sneaks through the veil to dwell in a physical body.

The veil is slightly porous which allows small amounts of spiritual energy to seep through into the physical. It's a one-way filter in that the physical

---

*This does not imply that other life forms don't have the equivalent of a human soul. All life forms maintain a connection with Spirit, all return to Spirit just as do humans.

cannot randomly cross back into Spirit. Only by undergoing a specific process can the physical return to Spirit: death for biological systems, collapse of the Universe for physical systems.

This seepage allows traces of Spirit to exist in the realm of the physical (spiritual resonance). Silent messengers cross back and forth at will. They leak spiritual imperatives to all creatures who are receptive to Intuition. This includes birds, rabbits, flowers, humans, all creatures large and small. They also lend knowledge and provide instructions to physical systems by telling atoms how to form molecules, how stars congregate to form galaxies. Silent messengers are couriers who broadcast knowledge direct from Unity. He or she who listens to Intuition has access to the Creator.

Other spiritual energies seep through the veil to form a halo, or aura around all biological life forms. The aura glows and lights the darkness which would otherwise surround animate matter. It also provides spiritual nourishment to those residing in the physical. Humans don't monopolize this energy field. A tree has its special form of aura, as does a mouse, a sparrow, an elephant. Nature, the physical manifestation of Unity, protects and nurtures all life forms. She has no favorites, each individual of every species receives its unique needs. We might suspect that elements and minerals also have an aura, a cosmic energy field that tells them how to act and react. Spirit, through Nature, directs affairs in the physical universe, all systems animate and inanimate.

The Outer Universe—The Physical

Back in Chapter Five we used Fig. 5-1 to graphically

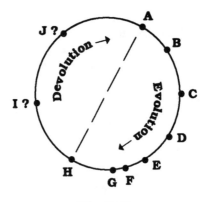

Fig. 8-3

depict a closed repetitive cycle. We briefly outlined a closed universal cycle—from the initial condition, expansion, contraction back to the initial condition.

Many things of special interest to earthly beings occur between points B and C during the universal cycle as shown by Fig. 5-1 (page 102). This brief segment of the universal cycle is expanded and shown by Fig. 8-3 to show Earth as a closed subsystem.

At point A, Earth and the other planets form shortly after birth of the Sun. On Earth, spiritual influences begin molding the surface in preparation for coming life. Between points A and B, conditions are extremely harsh. Earth is still receiving a continuous bombardment from cosmic debris, scorching radiation from the Sun blisters the surface, poison gasses erupt from the interior. From points B to C, Earth's surface begins cooling, an atmosphere of toxic gases form, water precipitates to form oceans.

Beginning at point C, Spirit begins exerting increased influence upon things to come. By some process unknown to us, primitive microbial life forms appear in the oceans. Silent messengers direct them to evolve slowly and propagate through all the oceans.

Microbes gradually develop into more advanced life forms, until at point D, fish begin populating the oceans. As time wears on, amphibians crawl up on land to later become reptiles. At point E, mammals appear. Silent messengers are now able to do in a few thousand years what previously required millions of years. Advancing life forms become ever more sophisticated at an accelerating rate. Primates appear at point F, with point G representing present time. Beyond point G, we are looking into the future. If observed trends continue, the interval from point G to indeterminate point H will witness a proliferation of higher life forms. (Point H does not necessarily indicate the mid-point of the cycle concerning elapsed time).

Point H is also an unhappy event for all biological systems. By then Sun will be running short of fuel and begin its expansion. The atmosphere will slowly deteriorate, Earth's surface temperature will gradually rise, infrared and ultraviolet radiation will increase, eventually the oceans will boil dry. Without water, the last microbe will go into extinction. At point J mountains will melt, Earth's surface will become a bubbling pot of molten rock. As the temperature continues to increase, Earth will vaporize into a cloud of dust and gas. The cycle comes back to point A, the initial condition again prevails.

Earth is gone, the solar system is dead, Sun shrinks to become a white dwarf, all biological life forms have returned to Spirit. Life must wait for another Big Bang or universal cycle to visit the physical again. How long will it have to wait?—many billions of years as we measure time while in the physical, a mere twinkling of the eye while in Spirit because Einstein told us that time doesn't exist apart from space and matter. Therefore, it would be waste of time to now take harp instructions to help pass the time while waiting to observe the next universal cycle.

Referring to his no boundary proposal, Stephen Hawking asked, "What place, then, for a creator?" Let's see what happens when we mentally superimpose *Earth's Cycle* (Fig. 8-3) over the *Dual Universe* symbol (Fig. 8-2). Lo, there at the center lays Unity. The Creator is Unity!, infinite energy, eternal wisdom, pure love. The Creator is an essence without beginning, without end; He/She just exists and will continue through eternity. We must therefore dismiss the question, "What came before the Creator?" As Joseph Campbell might have said, the nature and essence of the Creator is an Absolute Unknowable. The Creator just is, always has been, always will be.

The myth now contains provisions for the evolution of the Universe and our planetary home. It's a bit more graphic and detailed than Genesis, but the content says about the same thing providing one gives a liberal interpretation to the Biblical account. In either case, we find the Creator central to all physical things.

The Human Life-Cycle

What about us, we as individuals, how do we fit into the myth? We need another symbol.

Fig. 8-4 shows the normal human life-cycle (the small circle) tangentially touching the veil which separates the physical from the spiritual. During physical life, we are ever so close, yet beyond or outside Spirit except for experiencing the influence of the universal spiritual aura.

Particles of the life-essence congregate near the veil, then at the appropriate time, a portion sneaks through the veil to reside in the physical. We'll call it the

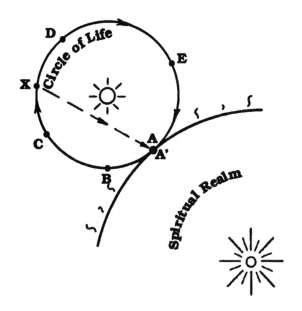

Fig. 8-4
Human Life-Cycle

A—Birth; B—Puberty; C—Adolescence;
X—Interruption of Life Cycle; D—Mid-Life;
E—Twilight Years;
A'—Physical Death and Return
to the Initial Condition

spark of life. It carries the essence of Spirit, it becomes a glowing core which illuminates the physical realm. This becomes the center around which each individual life revolves. It remains at the center of life, it influences us every day. Contained within the core of life is a blueprint which carries instructions (morphic fields?) telling life how to evolve, whether it becomes a rose, a bacteria, a snake, or a human in this case.

At point A, one steps across the veil from Spirit onto the wheel of physical life. We call it birth. The soul remains in Spirit hovering at Point A'.* The Soul waits, watches, and guides one around the circle of life. It summons the assistance of silent messengers requesting that they cross the veil conveying vital information essential to life—some of which we either don't hear or simply ignore. We probably cause soul much grief as we travel the circle because Intellect often leads us in the wrong direction. But we've got to learn, and mistakes are sometimes the best teacher. Soul must be patient with us, allowing us to learn by doing and profiting from error.

The journey from A to B represents a helpless state of being where one is completely dependent upon others for basic physical needs. It's a transition period where one separates from Spirit and grows into the physical. Soul, yearning for a deeper association with Spirit, may at this point regret having placed us in the physical. But then as we begin learning how to communicate in the physical, how to attend body functions, how to move about in the world, soul grows more comfortable with the situation. It is also learning.

From points B to C one develops physically from infancy, past puberty, into adolescence. Formal education begins, Intellect develops, one learns the customs and traditions of society. It's a confusing time, still part child, not quite adult. Sexual instincts surface, we exhibit rebellion, we begin to explore the numerous facets of life. At long last we learn to be a self-autonomous individual. At point C we enter early adulthood. Soul has resigned itself to our physical imprisonment though it still yearns for Unity. Our subconscious

---

*This doesn't mean that soul is way out yonder somewhere. It coexists with consciousness, but in another dimension.

detects this melancholy and subtly leads us into a search for our higher purpose.

Point X can occur at any point around the circle of life. It is a terminal interruption of the normal life cycle resulting from accident or disease. At premature death, consciousness instantly jumps the gap back to Point A' to rejoin the waiting soul. This situation leaves soul in a quandary. It longs to rejoin Unity but its earthly lessons are incomplete; soul has not learned what it sent us into the physical to experience. It must make a decision.

The soul has two options: reincarnate again into the physical to complete its lessons, or remain near the veil hoping to learn physical lessons by observing someone else, a sort of tag-along technique. It's not an easy choice. Soul would much prefer to stay in Spirit closer to Unity, but observation is not equivalent to experience. It may need to tag in the shadow of several other persons to witness the lessons it needs. This is a slow way to learn which delays ascent to higher levels in the Spiritual Realm. Soul's decision may depend upon how far it progressed while in the physical; that is, if the normal life-cycle terminated early in life, soul might elect to come back to Earth for another incarnation. This might be the case for infants, adolescents, and young adults. If, however, it had reached physical mid-life, it might decide to stay in Spirit and tie the loose ends together by watching other physical beings.

Mid-life, point D, represents the crown of individual activity. Formal education is complete and applied to the art of living. Careers have become well established, our children are either adolescents or young adults, we begin to experience prosperity, physical and mental abilities function in unison, we enjoy the most productive stage of life. Soul is now more at ease with the physical because it is learning things inaccessible while in the Realm of Spirit.

Point D also signifies reversal of the physical cycle. Vitality begins ebbing, ambitions become more focused, we have fewer options, it marks a general slowing down of the physical system, it may announce the onset of physical ailments or disabilities. In contrast, the mental system acquires increasing acuity as the physical system declines. The abhorred "mid-life crisis" is in fact a demarcation for increased mental activity, a period of releasing youthful concepts and developing a mature philosophy of life. The mid-life crisis is a peek around the corner of life where one can foresee the end as well as draw upon the past. Any trauma suffered during the mid-life crisis comes from a reluctance to release the past and accept the provisional future.

Point E is a time when physical impairments or ebbing energy retards one's activities. We can think of this phase of life as retirement, a release from previous responsibilities, a time of mature introspection. Then is when spiritualism begins replacing recreational sex, or without either, men take to golf with funny little grassmobiles which whisper to one another. Most wives don't complain about golf, it takes men out of the house and out of their hair.

Some who suffer physical afflictions may at some point return to a condition resembling infancy, a state of helplessness requiring the equivalent of parental care. Though it may cause a problem for one's caretaker, soul now anticipates imminent return to Spirit. In cases of severe mental problems, soul remains unconcerned because consciousness continues undisturbed in another dimension.

The advanced years are a time for reflection, a time

of sublime serenity, a time when we must face physical mortality. Despite the negatives associated with senility, in the absence of disease the mental system not only remains intact, it achieves a higher state of subjectivity (in bygone times before youth became exalted and adored, wisdom was an attribute of the elderly). The problems that troubled us during early adulthood become trivial, the higher meaning of life comes into sharper focus. Soul begins to glow as it anticipates its return to Unity.

Reentry—Back Across the Veil

Finally, when one comes full circle to point A', there waits the soul eager and ready to carry one back to Spirit. Many religious traditions say it's dust to dust, ashes to ashes. If put into the context of a closed natural cycle, returning to Spirit is a return to the initial condition. Whichever, consciousness has returned to and again become a part of Spirit.

The final hours or days preceding physical death represent another transition period, a brief time during which the subconscious adjusts in preparation to depart the physical and return to Spirit. We may not consciously recognize impending death, but the soul knows. The soul foresees victory over the physical; its euphoria penetrates the veil and enters the subconscious mind. This often brings a quiet calm to those suffering a terminal condition. The soothing energy which ebbs from this euphoria can dull pain and produce a pseudo remission of symptoms. It can occur just hours before death, or in some cases, several days in advance.

I first encountered this phenomenon in a book I bought back in the 1970s. Unfortunately, I loaned the book to someone (I don't remember who), and as so often happens, the book never found its way back home. I don't remember the title or the author(s?). I do remember its basic message.

This book described a study conducted concurrently in the United States and India concerning the final hours of terminally ill patients. The investigator(s) interviewed a cross-section of doctors and nurses who took care of desperately ill persons, including the days and hours leading up to their death. I can't recall the exact percentages or other statistics, but the investigators reported a significant number of cases where a reprieve from pain and fear occurred not long before death arrived. The terminally ill often experienced a state of euphoria, sometimes followed by a drowsiness resulting in a deep sleep. Death usually came a short time later. The incidence rate was approximately equivalent in both the United States and India, suggesting that religious beliefs did not enter into the phenomenon.

The book also opened my awareness to the state of euphoria so often experienced by those preparing to return to Spirit. I began keeping a mental journal of similar instances. Since I can't quote any specifics from the book, I will relate a few examples of the phenomenon of which I am personally familiar.

The first concerns an elderly lady whom I shall call Lil. (That wasn't her real name and I will slightly alter the circumstances). Lil was a nice widow lady much loved and respected by everyone in the community. Her kitchen always smelled of fresh baked cookies, vegetables from her garden found their way to many dinner tables. Then Lil became ill. It later became necessary to commit her to hospital care. Her condition continued to deteriorate and her future appeared gloomy indeed.

One afternoon while leaving my office I encountered a member of Lil's family. He said that Lil had revived and sat on the edge of the bed all afternoon talking and laughing and recounting her life experiences. He was jubilant because of her improved condition; I experienced alarm. I went home and told my wife that Lil was preparing to cross-over. She agreed when I related the circumstances. We later learned that Lil had had a good dinner and laid back to sleep. She passed-over peacefully just before midnight.

One need not suffer pain and receive oxygen and intravenous injections for the soul to anticipate an imminent return to Spirit. A condition can be terminal without outward symptoms. An unexpected death is quite a shock to one's family, but the soul knows and it marks the path back to Spirit for those preparing to depart. I have two examples to illustrate this, both quite personal.

One evening I received a call from a favorite aunt informing me that another favorite aunt has just passed away. I was particularly sad because I had procrastinated in writing her, now it was too late. My only comfort lay in the knowledge that she didn't suffer a protracted illness; she merely lay down to rest one evening before dinner, fell asleep, and never woke up (a heart attack). Imagine my surprise to receive a letter from her the next day—postmarked the day before her cross-over. Had I not known, the letter would have sounded perfectly normal; reading it after the fact, it was a cheerful farewell.

My last example is about my Dad. He had retired some ten years earlier and moved to southern California. He and Mom lived in a trailer park for retired persons where they enjoyed the climate and many new friends. Then Mom began having problems. The doctors never formally diagnosed her condition, but the symptoms fit what we now know as Alzheimer's disease. After little more than a year Dad had to commit her to a nursing home because he was no longer able to care for her. He was very lonely even though he visited her every day and had the support of many kind neighbors.

My wife and I went out for dinner one Friday evening and upon our return one of our daughters said that Dad had called. Since it was late, I decided to return the call next morning. Dad rarely called unless it was an emergency, so I was uneasy all night concerning Mom. I called Saturday morning and I didn't expect good news. It was a pleasant surprise to hear a happy and cheerful voice when Dad answered. I immediately asked what was wrong and he said, "Oh, nothing. I just wanted to talk with you." I should have known, but I was so relieved that my red-flag failed to go up. We had a long talk, our last.

The next Tuesday my sister called, and I will never forget her first words, "Dad is gone." I went numb. If a god ever walked on Earth, his tracks would have led directly to my Dad. Next, I wondered how Mom could get along without his support.

A neighbor last saw Dad the Monday afternoon before puttering in his yard. That Tuesday morning, after failing to answer his telephone, two neighbors went in and found him sitting in his chair in front of the television. He had apparently fallen asleep the evening before and suffered a heart attack. After the funeral, several neighbors told me that he had spent the preceding weekend going around seeing each of them (subconsciously saying farewell). They said he was in high spirits, the most jovial they had seen him since Mom fell ill.

Is there such a thing as soulmates? I don't know, but consider this: Mom followed Dad into Spirit about six weeks later. I lost them both within a short time, but it was comforting to know that they soon rejoined.

The soul knows. It anticipates our return to Spirit. And the nearer we approach that time, the more joyful our soul becomes. During the final days and hours that joy becomes so overwhelming that it completely captures the subconscious mind. The subconscious comes into dominance for the first time in life, the conscious mind fades into the background of Being. We subconsciously sense that our spirutual guide is waiting just across the veil with open arms. The cross-over is not a dreaded event; it is a completion, a grand reunion, a homecoming.

Bear in mind that Fig. 8-4 is symbolic. Don't get the idea that the Realm of Spirit is way out beyond the physical Universe; Spirit is an energy field contained within the Universe. Spirit is everywhere, it surrounds us, it fills us. We are Spirit, an eternal spark from Unity which just now happens to be wearing a physical cape.

Back In Spirit

Now, to continue the myth. Fig. 8-4 shows the wheel of life tangentially touching the Spiritual Realm wherein lays Unity. We postulated that the soul remained behind at point A' when we entered the physical. Then, after traversing the wheel, we again rejoined the waiting soul; or, in the case of premature death, we instantly shot the gap back to point A'. We then concluded that soul expressed profound joy when we returned to merge again with Spirit.

Was this joy misplaced, was soul yet subject to judgement and possible condemnation? No, it remained in Spirit, it is not accountable for our earthly deeds. It had maintained its spiritual connection with Unity all the while we were in the physical. Soul need not be *saved* because it was never in jeopardy. It is a spark which emanates from Unity, it will again return to the initial condition regardless of what we did or said. Our earthly actions may invoke consequences which need resolution before ascending into higher levels within Spirit, but that's a spiritual chore removed from physical being.

Soul knows that work is yet to be done, that it must prepare itself for rejoining Unity. Though it be our bridge back to eternity, it knows that immediately after returning from the physical we are not yet ready to return to the Source. Just as soul had to go through a transition period following our birth into the physical, it must now readjust to full-time existence in Spirit.

Many religions and mythological traditions have long recognized the existence of a transitional period. It's an intermediate step from the physical into the hereafter—however one conceives the hereafter. Some traditions refer to it simply as a state of limbo. Purgatory is the Catholic version, in Tibetan Buddhism the dead pass through several levels of "bardo" during which they receive instructions for reincarnation back to physical life. The half-way house concept is an old idea carried forward by many belief systems; it's an idea worth retaining in the myth.

We will think of the transition as a period of purification, a removal of residual physical energies. Like a dusty coal miner going to the shower after emerging from the shaft, we also must cleanse ourselves of physical impurities to allow the brightness of Spirit to shine through. Soul therefore does not immediately ascend to Unity, it must first polish its spiritual

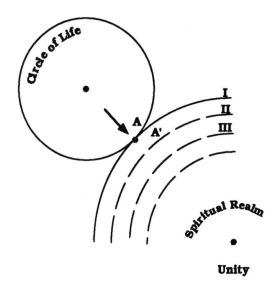

Fig. 8-5
Transcendent Dimensions

image.

    Accordingly, the transition zone lays just inside the Spiritual Realm. Beyond the transition zone, higher dimensions exist, each ascending level located nearer Unity. We can show these ascending levels by magnifying the contact zone at point A-A', shown on Fig. 8-4.

    Fig. 8-5 is an enlargement of the contact between the physical and Spiritual Realm. The dashed arcs inside the Spiritual Realm represent an ascending order of higher spiritual levels.

    Immediately after reuniting with soul we find ourselves at level I having the opportunity to loaf around, to rest, to meet with friends and loved ones. Here we review and analyze our physical life and just catch our spiritual breath so to speak. Perhaps it's within this zone that Dr. Moody's NDErs find themselves (they had crossed into Spirit but not yet released physical attachments). The transition zone is peaceful, without pain and emotional trauma. It's merely a period of adjustment.

The next step toward Unity, though serene, involves increased spiritual activity. Upon entering level II one catches up on what they missed while in the physical. He or she delves deeper into an analysis of what they learned while on Earth. Here our vision is clear, without the distortion caused by prejudice and intolerance. We see things in a spiritual light, or as Black Elk phrased it: *seeing in a sacred manner.* This level emphasizes acquiring unconditional love and a continued quest for knowledge. We are fortunate in that we don't have to repeat the learning we acquired while in the physical because we carry this knowledge back into Spirit. Level two is akin to acquiring a degree in preparation for ascent to the next higher level.

Entry into level III becomes more sophisticated and complex. This is perhaps the level at which Black Elk found himself during his vision, where Richard Bucke experienced his moment of Bhramic Bliss. It is an enlightened zone where love and wisdom prevail. When ready, and soul will somehow know when it's ready, we ascend into this region. This is the residence of what the various traditions refer to as Guides, Ascended Masters, Guardian Angels, the Enlightened Ones, or whatever.

Here the soul takes on the duty of assisting, or informing, entities who are struggling through an earthly existence. Guides or Guardian Angels attempt to inform those still in the physical by sending silent messages through the veil. Their voice is soft and gentle. They make no demands, they only give helpful suggestions and reveal vital information. But of course, while on Earth, we seldom pay much attention to our inner ear—our jealous Intellect interferes. Occasionally though, as we learn to trust Intuition, we do hear and heed warnings and words of advice.

It's from level three that we, while in the physical, receive impressions which we interpret as being memories from a previous lifetime. Our Guide sends this knowledge because it is pertinent to a life problem or situation. It is an invasion into another person's consciousness who lived in past times (spiritual morphic resonance, borrowing Sheldrake's terminology). We briefly become attached to that personality to experience its emotions and life's lessons. The experience of others in a like circumstance can provide valuable information. We can view their mistakes, grieve for their pain, witness how they handled a similar situation, better understand our present situation. Such knowledge keeps us on track without having to wander through the hinterlands of life.

Hypnotic pastlife regression therapy is often quite effective in relieving pain and emotional symptoms (Dr. Weiss gives many examples in *Through Time Into Healing*, as does Dr. Moody in, *Coming Back*). It works because Spirit Guides direct the subconscious toward pertinent episodes of the past which relate to a present condition. "Other-life therapy" is a better term.

Rectifying Mistakes

Where do Hitler and others who grossly violated spiritual imperatives fit into the scheme? Fundamentalists would say that the likes of such proceed immediately to hell where they reside through eternity. Conventional reincarnationists would have them return to physical life on Earth in order that they experience the grief they inflicted on others—a balancing of karma (something of an eye for an eye situation, albeit a learning process as opposed to retribution). By now it should be apparent that the Fundamentalist position is impossible according to the terms of my myth. I have already stated my doubts concerning conventional reincarnation theory: the number problem.

However, in Chapter Seven, we postulated possible exceptions where reincarnation theory may apply. Then earlier in this chapter, the myth provided a possible exception for those who die prematurely due to accident or disease before completing a normal-life cycle. That is, the soul had a choice concerning whether it remain in Spirit or reincarnate. The myth speculated that the soul of those who die young may elect to return to physical life whereas the soul of those who die after mid-life might choose to remain in Spirit.

So, where will Hitler and others of like mind end up? Since we all make mistakes in life, we must have an opportunity to rectify our errors. Divine forgiveness is indeed a convenient concept because it provides relief from personal responsibilities, but I doubt that it works that way. Mistakes incur consequences which lead to opportunity, new ways of learning and modified behavior. Errors accrue to one's benefit; being swept aside by divine intervention would deprive us of a learning opportunity. So, according to terms of the myth, Hitler certainly had (has?) unlimited opportunities.

When Hitler stepped from his bunker into Spirit, he no doubt found himself at level one where millions of his victims were still resting. I'm sure he was quite uncomfortable being in the company of those he had recently considered inferior. But, being in the presence of abounding love and wisdom, his earthly prejudice would soon dissipate and he would begin to regret his recent indiscretions. He would become his own judge, he would deliberate to arrive at his own verdict. Then having judged himself, he would impose sentence.

Though we can reasonably presume that Hitler was well past mid-life, his soul still had two choices: remain in Spirit, or return to physical life. Returning to physical life would have many benefits for those who never profited from error. If his soul elected to return to Earth, it could choose a life of suffering and persecution as a way of understanding how his many victims experienced physical life. Or, it might choose to go back and become a humanitarian, a martyr, an exalted leader liberating persecuted people. Spirit doesn't seek retribution, it strives for knowledge and wisdom and compassion. Neither does Spirit harbor grudges and prejudice; its goal is completion and perfection. Therefore, it's logical to think that a soul would choose the earliest and most expeditious opportunity to compensate for earthly indiscretions.

Remaining in Spirit is the other alternative for souls so unlucky as to have wasted their life on Earth. They may ascend to level two which is a period of intense learning for all of us. Here they must discard earthly ideas and attitudes, spiritual concepts must become deeply ingrained. They know that entry into level three is conditional. That is, they must develop into Masters before ascending higher, before returning to Unity. Hitler, and others who inflicted hardship upon Spirit, have some tough lessons to learn but being in the presence of unconditional love will bring about a transformation. As they learn, their soul will take on the radiance of Spirit.

Then, eventually reaching level three, their self-imposed sentence may stipulate that they become the Guide/Guardian Angel of another person in the physical who is following in their earthly footsteps. They have experience in such matters, they understand how dictators and criminals think. What better way to utilize their earthly experience? If there is any retribution involving their despicable earthly conduct, it comes from the defiance and rebellion exhibited by those under their spiritual leadership. This is how they learn patience and toleration.

Back To Unity

What happens when one completes his/her assignment on level three? My imagination breaks down at this point. I suspect that higher dimensions exist where soul prepares to shed its unique identity in preparation for rejoining Unity. Spiritual energies would dominate, physical memories would fade. Reality in this realm exceeds the scope of human conception, it is far too elegant and grandiose for our comprehension. All that we can know with certainty is that soul will somehow experience a grand reunion with Unity, to eventually lay snuggled up against the Creator.

All dualities vanish at Unity. The yin/yang, female/male attributes merge to become the One which resides at the core of Unity. The righteousness of a physical God cancels, or neutralizes, the evil of Satan. Heaven demolishes hell, love erases hate, spacetime evaporates into eternity, compassion overcomes greed, exclusiveness yields to the inclusiveness of Unity.

Unity doesn't consist solely of human life substance, it contains the essence of *all* life forms. This includes all those species which have fallen into extinction, those who are yet to evolve. It includes other life forms which may exist in the Universe plus the substance of galaxies and stars and solar systems. We are as One, we come from a common Source, we all return to that Source.

While in Spirit, the life essence of a duck is little different from that of a microbe, that of a human similar to that of a flea. Even while in the physical the biological differences are minute. Biologists tell us that the basic body building process is similar for all organisms; that is, we are a conglomeration of self-replicating cells with the difference in form being a matter of cell arrangement and complexity. We receive the instructions for the final form not long before incarnating into the physical. We carry these instructions across the veil because we each have an assignment, we adopt a form designed to perform specific tasks. Then after returning to Spirit, we relinquish this form when ascending to above level three. Ducks and fleas and humans become indistinguishable.

We might wonder: will microbes at some evolutionary stage become elephants, fleas become human? I don't know, but I can't see any reason why their soul should have such aspirations. It's only humans who claim exalted species status. Why should I think Pete, my dog, would trade places? He lays in the shade while I mow the lawn, he rides up front in the raft while I do the rowing, he doesn't put gasoline in the pickup after a ride. Why should fleas care to be humans, or microbes, elephants? Such questions again call up the subject of consciousness. Since we can scarcely define or understand human consciousness, how could we know the mind of a flea, a dog, an elephant? We can remain curious about such matters, fortunately, knowing the answers isn't crucial to living the myth.

Moreover, the myth states that the Creator doesn't accord humans any special prestige. He/She cherishes all life, each life form is equally important in the grand scheme. Furthermore, lest we become intoxicated with species importance, consider the likelihood of even higher life forms evolving, both here on Earth and throughout the Universe. Anthropologists a few million years hence may classify *homo sapiens* as an archaic prototype leading to their species. What place for us then?

To satisfy curiosity, I once had a psychic reading where this person was supposedly able to communicate with a higher being (known as channeling). She said that I could ask a question and that the informed being would provide an answer. I asked a question which I have long pondered: do animals have a soul, and if so, where was my departed German shorthair pointer named Cowboy, the dog I had before Pete? Such a mundane question apparently rattled this informed being. Most people want to know about relationships, financial security, matters of an exclusive nature. A considerable pause ensued, after which this high being said, "yes, animals have a soul but they exist in another dimension." That wasn't particularly enlightening because I had already decided that animals inhabit Spirit as well as humans, and that the Spiritual Realm had several dimensions. Further questioning didn't shed any light on that other dimension, it's just some place other than where humans go (more species chauvinism?). Maybe so? But my myth says that all dimensions (levels) merge at Unity. I expect that Cowboy and Pete will have their noses to the trail leading me back Home.

The Realm of Spirit is our natural home. Our brief journey into the physical is a temporary state of Being. We come from Spirit, we return to Spirit. We again join and become a tiny spark of the One, of Unity, of the Creator.

Chapter Nine

LIVING THE MYTH

Requiring Diligence, Understanding
And
Acceptance Of What Is

I like to rise early in the morning and sit quietly thinking about things that become drowned out later when the television starts blaring and the phone ringing. My early hour or two of solitude kind of hooks me back up to nature and the order of life giving me a better perspective for the coming day.

Several summers ago I sat looking out the window of our mountain cabin while sipping coffee and watching the rising sun send its light down the slopes of Elk Mountain in Glacier National Park just a mile or so north. A whitetail doe and fawn were browsing at the edge of a small meadow directly in front of the cabin. Also absorbing my attention was a male cliff swallow shuttling back and forth to the willow lined creek just beyond the meadow. This industrious little fellow was bringing insects to his mate who nestled over her eggs in a mud constructed nest under the eaves of the roof overhanging the front deck of the cabin.

It was early summer and for several weekends we had watched both birds patiently carrying little dabs of mud and dry grass making the nest. We hadn't posted a "For Rent" sign, but if they were aware that they were trespassing, they also knew that they were welcome guests. This particular morning, after having brought his mate breakfast, the male perched on the railing around the deck just outside my window. He sat perfectly still, back to me, and rested while he soaked up the sunshine which by now had just reached the cabin.

I got up to refill my coffee cup and, Prissy, our cat came out from behind the couch where she usually slept. She stretched and went to the door indicating that she wanted outside. I saw through the door window that my friend the swallow, looking much like an orchestra director in black tails and gleaming white breast, was still presiding over his territory from the deck rail. I hesitated to let Prissy out, but I thought—that rail is over three feet high and she can't catch that bird. So, I opened the door and let her out. My little conductor looked back over his shoulder to see what the disturbance was and then went back to directing the affairs of nature.

Prissy stretched out on the door mat in the sun, I went back to the table with my coffee, the two deer are by now back in the timber where they will bed for the day, and my morning reverie is about over. Suddenly I see a gray and white streak (Prissy) arching through the air toward my orchestra leader. In a split second she had the bird and dropped back to the deck. I dashed out the door, grabbed Prissy, and pried her jaws open with my thumb and forefinger. A lump of ruffled feathers fell to the deck and Prissy gets thrown back into the cabin.

I left the bird lay and went inside to consider his prognosis. After a few minutes he wobbled to his feet and sat there stunned, looking about like I felt when I fell out of my Grandfather's hayloft and broke my wrist some 35 or more years earlier. By then my coffee was cold but the little bird seemed to be gaining strength. In a few more minutes he lifted off and glided over to a pine tree out in the yard about 25 feet away. I felt pretty good about the outcome but Prissy was grumpy all day and didn't lay on my lap that evening.

A week or so later my wife Nancy, Matt our 12 year old grandson, and I went back to the cabin for a few days. The first thing I checked was our tenants under the eve. I could see the beak and head of the expectant lady as she sat cramped in the little nest. The proud gentleman, dressed in tails, guarded his territory from the more secure perch of the pine tree beyond the reach of felines. We stayed a few days doing some fishing and rafting.

One evening all three of us were sitting on the deck listening to the gurgling creek off in the willows and watching a small herd of elk on the mountain above the cabin. A cool breeze carried the scent of pine and fir pollen and it was apparently dinner time for the expectant lady overhead. The gentleman of the family would swoop in under the eaves, hover a moment transferring the bug in his beak to his mate, and then fly off again for another morsel.

Our little provider ducked from under the roof starting another trip, when from seemingly nowhere, and quick as a silent bolt of lightning, a prairie falcon dived down with outstretched talons and snatched the little swallow in mid-flight. A little puff of dark blue feathers drifted down right in front of us and the falcon with his prey disappeared into the timber.

We three on the deck sat stunned. Then Matt jumped up, a tear in the corner of his eye, and said, "Grandpa, do something!" Of course, it was another of those times in life, when regardless of how omnipotent we tend to view ourselves, there wasn't anything that could be done. For all our smarts, despite all our technology, nature will work her own way and bend us to her will. We all felt bad and it kind of ruined our evening. We wondered about *our* lady—would she be able to forage for herself, would her instinct to procreate override the instinct for self-survival and she therefore starve protecting her eggs?

The incident was a lesson in perspective. To the three humans sitting on the deck it was a tragedy. We had lost a friend, a little dark blue and white bird with whom we had become personally attached. We fretted about his lady and the possible destiny of their offspring. We never did know the outcome: when we returned a couple weeks later the female was gone leaving no evidence of egg shell fragments suggesting a successful hatch. I felt particularly humbled because in the end I couldn't save my friend.

If animals and birds were capable of rational thought and articulate speech, Prissy might have said, "So what. If you had left me alone I would have had fresh bird for breakfast the other day, but no, the falcon got him instead." The falcon, as he swooped away with his prey, no doubt felt proud because now his family would have a meal this evening. If he had known the background, he might have wondered, "I don't understand humans. It's perfectly okay if swallows eat insects, but they make me out the villain if I feed my family swallows. Moreover, I saw a couple of them along the creek today catching fish to eat. Who do they think they are, God?"

Sometimes that little bird still comes to mind. It's more than just the memory of an incident, it feels something like an attraction, a bond which connects us as one. I think he flutters through my consciousness to remind me of things so easily forgotten. For one thing, he reminds me that we are both connected to the same Source, and through this mutual interconnection we in essence share the same universal life force and ultimate destiny. His memory also reminds me that I have no spiritual authority to assign priorities to any of nature's creatures. As the Creator views things, a falcon is as important as a swallow, a man is no better than either. We all have a place in nature, we all serve a purpose otherwise we would not be here.

Life Sustains Life

The incident was also a vivid enactment of a natural imperative which has long troubled philosophers; that is, life eats life. I don't know where the food chain begins or where it ends, or if it even has a beginning or ending. It's more like a loop, the snake eating its tail. We often think of large creatures eating smaller ones, but this isn't necessarily true. Man eats creatures a lot larger than himself (thanks to weapons) while at the same time he falls prey to the smallest of creatures—bacteria, viruses, microorganisms. It's not a one-way street where bigger and smarter are better, we are all simultaneously predators and victims. Life doesn't eat life, life *sustains* life. Said another way, all creatures depend upon all other creatures; if one link in the food chain becomes weak or broken, it effects all of us adversely, either directly or indirectly.

We are destined to eat one another, that's the way the system works. Vegetarians sometimes look down upon those of us who eat meat. That's okay if they don't like meat, or it doesn't agree with them, but let them not assume that they are sparing a life. A kernel of wheat, a coffee bean, and an egg all contain the life-force; if not consumed for breakfast, a kernel of wheat can produce seeds for fifty stalks of waving grain, a coffee bean can produce another plant, an egg can become a chicken. To spare the chicken and eat the egg is somewhat hypocritical, or foregoing the egg and having toast and coffee is also dubious reasoning: can anybody rightfully say that the Creator cherishes a chicken more than a stalk of wheat or coffee plant?

Orthodox nutritionists tell us to forego red meat, that it isn't good for us. They no doubt learned this from some over-weight and under-exercised professor who doesn't practice what he or she teaches. These experts may be partly right (stay away from marbled fat), but I suspect that they fail to consider that each of our bodies have different requirements. And this variation may relate to genetics (or morphic fields).

For instance, my north European ancestors were hunter-gatherer people up until about fifty or so generations back. They subsisted primarily on red meat, fish, and fruits and berries. These happen to be my favorite foods. I also eat vegetables and dairy products, but my body likes a lot of protein and fructose. I'm not sure that even my doctor agrees with my hypothesis, but I think that what the body craves is what it needs. Since I've been relatively healthy all my life, I don't pay much attention to television experts who prescribe my daily minimum requirements.

On the other hand, those who descended from agrarian cultures reaching back two hundred generations or more might prefer cereals, vegetables, and dairy products since their metabolic system has evolved to better digest these foods. The diet of our ancestors may influence our likes and dislikes, which in turn determines the types of food the body can best assimilate. Pete and Prissy adhere to this hypothesis: both of their immediate ancestors are carnivorous and Prissy would rather have bird for breakfast than toast, and Pete doesn't like carrots any better than I.

This myth doesn't discriminate between species because every life form from the tiniest microbe to the largest whale carries the same life-force, a spark bestowed by the Creator. It's beyond my spiritual authority to say I am more important to the grand scheme than the spider which spun a web around my neglected yard tools. When eating a T-bone steak, I realize that it is a part of a creature that once lived. But I also realize that if cows were not bred and raised for eating purposes, that critter would never have had life—ranchers don't keep herds just for the fun of it. So, is it better to have never lived, or to have a life which serves others? The Creator seems to have decreed the latter.

The fact remains, life sustains life. Excepting a few minerals (salt, for instance), everything in a grocery store is organic (wasteful packaging excluded). We all depend upon one another, that's how the Creator designed the system.

Perhaps not all environmentally conscious people sanctify plant life as much as they do animate life. I'm not sure that we should usurp the intent of the Grand Scheme in this respect. Grass and plants are a fundamental part of the food chain, trees and plants also supply the oxygen we animate creatures require. I loathe cutting a tree even though I do so to serve purely personal ambitions (clearing a spot for my house, for instance, or wood from which to build it). Every time I put my chain saw to the bark of a tree, I wonder: is it aware of what is about to happen, does it feel pain as the blade goes through its heart? Most will say no—trees don't possess consciousness, they don't feel pain. For my part, consensus opinion isn't worth much; in fact, it is usually wrong because the majority hasn't really given much thought to the issue. Despite this general apathy toward trees, I abhor cutting a Christmas tree because it is such a waste—it struggles 10 to 15 years to establish roots in rocky terrain only to be sacrificed for two weeks adorning my home. Yes, I'm aware of artificial trees, but according to superior domestic authority, they don't smell good. (I'm glad to say that this year we bought a plastic tree which will last for years to come).

Spiritualism vs Materialism

The myth holds that consumption of natural resources is essential to all life. The basic rule is: never harvest beyond need!* Trouble comes when need translates into extravagance or greed.

Both are an expression of compulsive materialism. But how can we change an economic system which relies entirely upon rapid depletion of natural resources and rampant consumption? Here I go, politicking, but that's sometimes essential when living the myth. For now, however, I leave this matter to the activists and will concentrate instead upon the sensitive interdependence inherent within nature.

Failure to recognize, or acknowledge, this fragile interdependence is a major weakness in the thinking of industrial societies. We take bountiful food supplies for granted. Who cares if we exterminate a few species in our quest for material comfort? When was the last time you had spotted owl for breakfast, or grilled a grizzly bear steak? And why worry about dolphins suffering injury or death in the nets of fishermen, after all, how

---

*The global population explosion enters into this problem, and unless we find suitable substitutes, our collective consumption will at some point exceed the supply.

many of us keep a dolphin in our aquarium?

We never slow up enough to realize that all creatures serve a purpose, we don't see the interdependence in nature. Our short term thinking leads us to adopt a hand-to-mouth attitude: if we don't need it for lunch tomorrow, don't worry about it. Our collective attitude and behavior denies all spiritual and physical fundamentals. This myth dismisses short-term thinking, it topples mankind from his self-acclaimed species superiority.

I don't carry banners and shout slogans when animal rights activists terrorize a community, I don't throw ink at ladies wearing fur coats, I don't vandalize laboratories in which mice are subjects for research, I am not a vegetarian. Such activities are self-destructive, distractions conceived by Intellect as an excuse to avoid walking the spiritual path. Blind activism misses the mark because, as with consensus opinion, most organizers haven't thought much toward the problem— no long term plans or suggestions.

Genuine activism advocates prudent utilization of natural resources, a deep respect for nature, acknowledgment of our dependence upon the most insignificant of creatures, protecting the environment, and the preservation of endangered species. But there is more to it than mere thinking and feeling. Consider timber harvest for example: to decrease the harvest is the last of many steps. First, we must find suitable substitute materials from which to build houses and furniture; second, the industrial complex must find ways to absorb unemployed lumberjacks. In short, all of society must become involved, we must find a new economic model, we must gear our actions to meet long-term objectives. Finally, we must incorporate these principles into our personal mythology. It's all easily enough said, living the myth is another matter.

The preceding are overt gestures one can make while traveling the path. Even more important to living the myth: nourish the inner-self! Forgive yourself as you forgive others, recognize the divinity within yourself and others, always remain in awe at the marvel of Being. Learn to accept what is, cease yearning for that which Intellect craves.

Dynamic Mythology As A Way Of Life

Aside from my deep abiding respect for nature, I don't literally believe much of my personal mythology. I just don't know the answer to most of my questions. I probably never will while here in the physical.

Neither have I cast my myth from a mold of dogma. A myth should be fluid and free-flowing, subject to alteration when new or additional knowledge becomes available. Any personal philosophy should be open-ended in that we allow old tattered ideas to drop off the trailing end while attaching new ideas to the leading edge. This, of course, requires that one remain ever willing to change their mind. Living the myth forbids one forming a mind-set based upon a single body of evidence. We must explore all avenues of knowledge, we must grade and sort all incoming information, we must analyze all new ideas and compare them to actual life experience and observations. Trusting Intuition is essential to keeping the myth fresh and alive. But, in the end and despite our best thinking, we must always acknowledge that we are delving into the Absolute Unknowable.

Separateness

Before going any farther, I must warn you: many people won't agree with the mystic image of Spirit which the myth portrays. Moreover, they refuse to surrender soul back to Unity because they don't want to lose their personal ego. Mary Jones and John Brown were promised a seat at the right hand of the Almighty, and by jove that's where they insist on going. From this exalted position they could look down upon those who insulted and humiliated them while in the physical. Retribution is only fitting, and having been judged worthy in the esteem of the High One, they will have their revenge. An eye for an eye and a tooth for a tooth, that's what they want.

Be that as it may, and despite their inherent limitations, personal myths do have value. They can prescribe limits of behavior, they can and do influence our personality, they can guide and direct our interaction with others, *they establish our relationship with nature.* This last criteria is of utmost importance because it goes beyond the teachings of most modern religions. (There are exceptions to the last statement: I quote one later).

Nature, the physical manifestation of Spirit, fell into the background of consciousness during the formative centuries of Western culture. Our religion and philosophy became increasingly exclusive; that is, personal concerns emphasized salvation of the soul, finding the gate to heaven, eluding the treachery of the wicked one with a forked tail.

Superstitions and fear based orthodoxy have waned in more recent times but exclusiveness (concern for self) remains in full career. We can define exclusiveness as materialism, aggressive competition, and general apathy toward nature and our fellow human beings. Economic matters receive high priority while nature weeps in neglect. The entire ecosystem is forlorn and dejected because of society's propensity to convert it into luxurious living. Personal mythology has the power and flexibility to revive nature, to forge a link between spiritual and physical being, to restore *inclusive* thinking to society at large.

Exclusiveness has crept gradually into society without much notice. Its presence appears daily on television and in newspapers. Despite the inner-city problems so often brought to our attention, most Americans are secure beyond the wildest dreams of most other nations. We have freedom and opportunities unimagined in Third World countries, wealth beyond their comprehension. Until of late, the United States was the world's economic and industrial leader. How did we get there, and why are we now declining in world prominence?

Up through World War II the United States had a collective mind-set based upon inclusiveness, the bringing together of people of every nationality. Europeans, Asians, South Americans, and other racial groups joined hands and pulled toward a common goal. The majority of those people were self-dependent, relying upon their wit and ambition to achieve the American dream. The melting-pot idea is an illusion, these were self-activating people, independent, willing and able to fulfill their individual dreams. Independent people think and act according to the principle of inclusiveness. Though each worked and lived in their own way, they were loyal to their country and to each other. If a man's barn burned, they all came together to raise another, if he fell sick at harvest time the neighbors came together and stacked hay in his loft. They shared a common dream, they pulled together toward that end. That's how we got where we were.

What happened after the War? I answer a very complex question with a simple statement: we moved away from inclusiveness toward exclusiveness. We became a nation bent on serving-self to the exclusion of others. If your barn burns, that's tough luck. We lost our unity of purpose choosing instead to pursue personal interests, often at the expense of others. When asked why America had so many problems, in one of his taped interviews Joseph Campbell replied to the effect, "We no longer have a national myth to live by."

Special interest groups have split the nation into thousands of exclusive cliques, each wanting something nobody else gets but everybody pays for. The media supports this fracturing of America by telecasting contesting groups at every opportunity. It's a polarization of society, presented such that we must take an emotional stand one way or the other: if I'm for one group, I alienate myself from the other. Meanwhile, as jobs move to overseas industry, the nation's wealth circulates within a closed system (Wall Street). These big boys are the most exclusive, and fearful, group in the country. Rather than placing capital at risk developing new ideas and more opportunities, the nation's wealth lays locked up in the stock of declining industries. These are some of the reasons why we are where we are.

It all boils down to short-term thinking, acting without considering the consequences, an unwillingness to plan for the coming generation. We are all guilty in one way or another. Plastic money contributes to our short-sighted view of the future: "go now, pay later" has become the national agenda. This attitude certainly precludes any hope of our children and grandchildren ever achieving prosperity—they are those who will pay later.

Coming Back Together

Our problems have been at least a half-century in the making, they can't be cured by some magical piece of legislation. In fact, government is completely helpless when it comes to solving problems of our magnitude (no, don't blame politicians for our situation—we asked for it). If any one solution exists, it amounts to people abandoning the exclusiveness of self-concern, of making the concern of others our concern. This means thinking less about **me**, more about **us**. If **we** all adopt this philosophy, **I** am automatically included. So, living the myth is about inclusiveness, not only within a nation, but throughout the global community.

The myth isn't really intended as a format to make political statements (as the preceding paragraphs), living it is a way of life, a bringing together, recognizing the central Source of all that is. It's better to keep Black Elk's vision in mind: the hoop of the people, the hoop of the nation, the great hoop of all nations. This is what inclusiveness is all about.

Fortunately, Black Elk's legacy still lives. One such person is Wallace Black Elk, also a Holy man of the Lakota people. Wallace Black Elk (our original Black Elk's first name was Nick) was born in 1921 on the Rosebud reservation in South Dakota. At age five, his elders determined that he study the old ways of his people. He studied under the tutelage of several wise grandfathers (spiritual, not necessarily blood kin), Nick Black Elk included, for the purpose of preserving the Lakota tradition. His training was long and rigorous and he did attain the powers of a shaman. In 1978 anthropologist William S. Lyon met Wallace thus beginning a twelve year association. From this alliance came a book, *Black Elk: The Sacred Ways of the Lakota.*[1]

I had the good luck to hear a talk given by Wallace Black Elk in the Spring of 1992. His humor, wit, and wisdom electrified the 400 or so who packed the small theater. He soon let us know that the word *Sioux* is the white man's name for his people, they refer to themselves as *Lakota* which in their language means *Earth People.* And Earth People believe that all life is sacred, including the two-leggeds, the four-leggeds, the feathered, and the creepers and crawlers. Among the two-leggeds, they do not differentiate between white and red, yellow or black. We are all brothers, offspring of Tunkashila, the Great Spirit. Thus, Wallace Black Elk continues the tradition of Nick Black Elk; that being, the great hoop includes all creatures including even the creepers and crawlers. The Lakota beliefs, centered around inclusiveness, provide a pattern for living the myth.

Reference to the two Black Elks does not imply that only the Lakota people lived this way. Inclusiveness, or concern for the tribe as a group, ran through all the Native American traditions. The old ways were good ways, the present squalor of reservation life so dutifully reported by the media resulted from stringent regulations imposed by the white settlers who invaded Indian territory. Exclusiveness, as practiced by well intentioned by grossly intolerant and ignorant missionaries, broke the spirit of the Red Man and methodically tried to destroy his native beliefs. To practice their calling, both Nick and Wallace had to go underground, meet in secret, remain wary of the reservation police. Not until 1978 could Indians legally practice their ancient rites. Fortunately, men and women like Wallace Black Elk have kept the old ways alive. Listening to their wise counsel is an inspiration for all.

A few pages back I promised a quote which is an exception to the teachings of most modern religions. The following is a classic definition of inclusiveness, it coming from Unitarian Universalist Minister Gary Kowalski, from his book, *The Souls of Animals*:[2]

> "When we relate to another [animals included] as a thing our experience is flat and lacking in depth. We never really share ourselves; we touch on the surface only. When we relate to others as spiritual beings, our experience opens into a "vertical dimension" that stretches toward infinity. Our world becomes softer and more intimate. We become confidants—literally, those who come together with faith. And it is through faith—not the faith of creeds or dogmas, but the simple "animal faith" of resting in communion with each other and with the natural world of soil and sunlight—that we touch the divine."

Now The Tough Part—Practice What You Preach

Living the myth therefore becomes a matter of association, a bringing together of divergent views, a merger of contesting interests. It begins with establishing a spiritual connection between ourselves and others. It involves a recognition of the connectedness and interdependence of all things animate and inanimate. In this regard, one could see Mother Earth as a living pulsating organism, the Universe as a grand macroorganism. Everything comes from a common Source, everything including the physical and spiritual will eventually return to from whence it came.

Soul is aware of this association as it hovers inside the veil waiting for us to return from the physical. It suffers embarrassment because of our ignorance when acting in a demeaning way toward other people and creatures. Anything we might do to desecrate nature is an insult to our Creator. To belittle a beetle is to mock the Source, to turn our back to those in need is to withhold from the Creator. He/She intends for us to walk in harmony with nature, not exploit her for personal pleasure—hello Mary Jones and John Brown, are you listening?

Oh, oh. I have just violated the terms of my myth. I have no spiritual authority to pass judgement on others or criticize their beliefs. Whether they acknowledge it or not, they came from the same Source as I. Sorry about that Mary and John.

This goes to show that creating a myth is a lot easier than living it. I must constantly remind myself to remain tolerant of other peoples' beliefs and persuasions. Nobody has the spiritual right to impose their beliefs, morals, and values upon another. There are many paths, many beliefs, many ways to model one's life. What works for one person may not work for another and we all have the right to decide for ourselves. If a path feels comfortable, follow it. If not, find another path. They all go in the same direction, they all terminate at the same place—back to Spirit.

My myth has only one inflexible rule: *Never knowingly do or say anything to cause injury to another.* This includes physical injury, insults, defamation of character, inflicting emotional trauma, racial and ethnic discrimination, trying to impose our will upon others. Every person walking the face of Earth came for a purpose, who gave me authority to dissuade them from their personal spiritual path?

This rule doesn't obviate my right to be selective concerning those with whom I wish to socialize. Most of us prefer intimate associations with those who harbor like interests, careers, hobbies, religious convictions, etc. I would personally feel more at ease with a group of engineers than attend a legal convention; not because I think engineers are any better than lawyers (a small fib for sake of diplomacy), but because each career field speaks a different language. But going on a fishing trip with a lawyer and a doctor would be different because we would then be participating in a common interest. (Incidentally, barbless hooks make fishing a sport which allows one to return the prey to the water without having to take its life).

We all have the spiritual right to select friends, mates, and other intimate associates; but we also have the responsibility of providing the same rights to others. Living the myth requires constant attention. We must remain open-minded, eliminate prejudice and intolerance from our attitudes, be considerate and tolerant of others outside our social-set. (Personal responsibility is grossly lacking in our national myth, something that needs cultivation).

Back To The Big Question—Why?

Now, having constructed a fanciful myth, I still haven't answered the questions: Why did the Universe come into being, did the emergence of life in ancient seas serve a purpose, why have so many species come into being only to suffer extinction, why did it take so long for conscious thinking creatures like mankind to evolve? If existence in the Spiritual Realm is so grand, why is life condemned to the rigors of physical existence? If the Creator is indeed the Source of pure love, why would He/She choose to send us across the veil to suffer hardship, pain, and disease? Or, if existence on the other side is as majestic as described by Richard

Bucke and the hundreds of Dr. Raymond Moody's NDEers, why would we voluntarily elect to cross over into the physical?

The NDEers themselves have answered this last question but we must still interpret its meaning. Those who have peeked through the veil into eternity come back sensing a duty, or yearning, to acquire knowledge and to learn unconditional love. But is this a contradiction in reason? Does it imply a lack of love and knowledge in the Spiritual Realm; and if so, how could the spiritual be so peaceful and serene without love and knowledge?

Some side-step this seeming breach in rationale with a statement such as, "we can learn some things only while in the physical." Now that's not very informative. It doesn't say "what things." We're therefore left to speculate concerning "those things." The speculation is this: knowing and loving in the spiritual is a given, a gift bestowed by the Divine; knowing and loving in the physical is an experience, the physical application of both, living the myth through tangible action.

We recall that all dualities will merge at Unity, and this includes both the spiritual and the physical. Therefore, we can further speculate that the spiritual and the physical each acquire a special kind of knowledge, and each loves in a unique manner. The blending of each at Unity brings the Source into balanced harmony, an integrated Whole which grows and expands as love and knowledge merge. The Creator is therefore not a static entity which measures out judgement with one hand and offers rewards with the other. He/She is dynamic and also ever evolving to higher levels of consciousness. Each of us act as envoys carrying tid-bits of knowledge and love back to the Source. This allows the Creator to continue evolving, always ascending to higher levels of perfection.

Therefore, I feel that it behooves me to learn as much as possible while in the physical, it may ultimately be of benefit to my Creator. And learning involves more than acquiring knowledge; it also includes acquiring the ability to love. Learning to love would include, but not necessarily be restricted to, toleration and respect of and for all creatures large and small. I don't really know why, or how, but the learning process feels like a spiritual imperative, a mission for which I was born. Yes, I've fallen short many times, but I try. Somehow, I think that effort and good intentions count because mistakes and omissions are also good teachers. Besides, if I were perfect, why bother to come into the physical?

Trying is what counts most. We all have differing abilities, varying degrees of curiosity, a special and personal mission. The important "thing" is to follow a path compatible with one's inherent abilities and aptitude. We can't learn everything there is to know, that's why there are so many of us. The laws of probability would say that our collective efforts will total up to what our Creator expects, and needs. He/She may also feel pain when we stumble and fall, but learning to walk tall is the nature of Creation.

Though we are not consciously aware of what happens, silent messengers work both sides of the veil. They not only bring us knowledge from Spirit, they also transmit knowledge and life's experiences from each of our lives back through the veil into Spirit. The collective total of all our thoughts and actions register in the universal data bank. This knowledge and experience helps form and shape Unity. It is a dynamical system, never static, always ascending to higher orders in the universal collective consciousness.

Destiny?

If this is the way the process works, it precludes the idea of divine destiny. Without an ordinate plan, it's as if the Creator were on a journey partaking of the joys which unfold each day, an adventure in Being with nature being His/Her invited guest. Let it proceed as it will, not much can go wrong. If allowed to follow a natural course, Spirit will also ascend to higher levels. Perhaps the Creator also longs for our return, He/She looking forward to a Grand Homecoming.

As for living the myth, it becomes a moot point whether the Universe collapses in the Big Crunch, expands into a heat death, or begins another cycle of expansion. Galaxies, stars, planets, and organisms are merely physical apparel which clad an eternal Essence. Perhaps the destiny of a physical Universe awaits a decision by the Creator, a choice He/She will make after the system returns to the initial condition. The flat model may represent flexibility in the mind of the Creator, not sloppy workmanship. He/She may choose to initiate another adventure, in which case the Universe will close. If not, the Universe will proceed toward the heat death, but all life will have returned to Spirit and lay snuggled up close to Unity.

I doubt that my myth will ignite an explosion in new thinking, that isn't its purpose. It is certain to be distasteful to those who have formed a mind-set. Some institutional religions may be critical because I have omitted much of the standard orthodoxy. Many people may have already formed their personal mythology, and that's okay. Besides, as stated at the out-set, my myth doesn't portend to convey literal truth. I do think that it gives me a generalized understanding of how "things" **may** function.

I **do** think that consciousness survives serious brain damage and physical death. I **do** think that at death, we all arrive at approximately the same place. Then, upon returning to Spirit, there will be no grading and sorting such as some will ascend to glory while others are forsaken. I **don't** think that consciousness and mind are material things contained in a bundle of neurons within the brain; they are knowledge and love, they collectively constitute an accumulation of thoughts and memories which survive time and pass into eternity. I **do** think that consciousness and mind (if they are not the same) have a direct connection to that of the Creator.

Most mythologies try to create a visual image of the Creator. This makes Him/Her more personal, more accessible, more familiar. At present, we are the most highly evolved species on Earth; therefore, it's only natural that we credit the Creator with having human-like characteristics. Our mental image facilitates prayer, it is a source of inspiration and hope, it provides a benevolent companion who leads us through life. We become quite comfortable with our image of the Creator.

In truth, while in the physical we cannot know the Mind and Essence of the Creator. These qualities shall forever remain the Absolute Unknowable. We may obligingly nod our head in affirmation when someone suggests that the Creator is a Spirit. Thus, we go from one Absolute Unknowable to another. The Essence of Spirit is as elusive as that of the Creator; yet we sense its existence, we feel its influence. This sensing, this influence, crept into the consciousness of prehistoric man, it has come forward in one form or another to present times. It has become the backbone of all mythologies and religions.

In a broad sense, the myth parallels the mythologies of old. It's an update to include some of the new information acquired during the past few decades. If new knowledge comes along, the myth must undergo revision to make it consistent with future discoveries or revelations. For now, I consider modern paranormal experiences as legitimate as the prophesies and revelations handed forward from antiquity. For example, the near death experiences reported by Dr. Raymond Moody, the moment of Bhramic Bliss recounted by Richard Bucke, the vision of Black Elk, and all scientifically unexplainable phenomena are brief glimpses into Spirit, into eternity.

Having a myth is what's important, developing a pathway or model for life which feels comfortable. It need not be Absolute Truth, that's beyond earthly possibility. We can't know everything, we can't be correct all the time, mistakes and deficiencies are part of the human condition. The soul does seek perfection; unfortunately that isn't likely to happen while yet in the physical. But having a myth keeps us on track, it provides a vision of one's ultimate goal. Then having developed a personal myth, live it!

A word of caution: don't become so preoccupied with constructing a myth that you neglect nourishing the inner-self, and that of others. Once you learn to love and accept yourself, you will begin seeing the divinity in others, in nature.

Living the myth is a full-time endeavor, it requires constant self-supervision. It is more than being guarded concerning one's actions and interactions, it must become second nature, a way of life. It is walking through life hand-in-hand with Spiritual Awareness, listening to Intuition and heeding its wise counsel. It is experiencing the personal transformation which comes into Consciousness as one abandons exclusiveness and moves toward inclusiveness. Some may achieve the Enlightenment, most of us can be quite content living in the light of Wonderment.

Some of this myth came from natural science, some is imaginary, the most important parts are, "some things that a little bird told me."

> *To know is to be free,*
> *and with freedom comes*
> *joy and love and divine bliss.*

Appendix

Notes and References

Foreword

NOTE:

1. From Peter Bishop & Michael Darton, Editors, *The Encyclopedia of World Faiths*, 1987, Facts On File Publications.

Chapter One

NOTES:

1. This discussion isn't intended as scientific discourse on Big Bang theory and cosmology. For those interested in more details, listed below are a few books written by scientists slanted toward lay readers.

   Isaac Asimov, *The Universe: From Flat Earth to Black Holes and Beyond*, Third Edition, 1980, published by Walker and Company.

   Paul Davies, *The Runaway Universe*, 1978, Harper & Row
   _____,*God and the New Physics*, 1983, Simon & Schuster
   _____,*The Mind of God: The Scientific Basis For A Rational World*, 1992, Simon & Schuster.

   Alan Lightman and Roberta Brawer, the 49 page introduction to, *Origins: The Lives and Worlds of Modern Cosmologists*, 1990, Harvard University Press.

   William J. Kaufmann, *Black Holes and Warped Spacetime*, 1979, W.H. Freeman and Company.

   John Gribbin and Martin Rees, *Cosmic Coincidences: Dark Matter, Mankind, and Anthropic Cosmology*, 1989, Bantam Books.

   David Layzer, *Constructing the Universe*, Scientific American Library, distributed by W.H. Freeman and Company.

2. In 1964 physicist Robert Dicke predicted that if there had in fact been a Big Bang, a remnant (or background) of radiation should still exist. The next year, 1965, Arno Penzies and Robert Wilson, of Bell Telephone Laboratories, detected this radiation. This discovery gave considerable support to Big Bang theory.

3. Absolute zero is the coldest anything can become. There's no upper limit on how hot something can be, but temperature can never go below –273° C or –460° F.

4. This term comes from the second law of thermodynamics, and as here used it is a measure of the disorder in a system. Heat (energy) still exists but it is in an unuseable state—diluted, or widely dispersed through broad regions of cold space.

    Think of a match for instance: its head contains the potential to produce heat. When struck, it releases a flare of energy to ignite a stove or light a candle, after which its energy disperses throughout the room. Its released energy still exists but is in a useless form. Though its energy is conserved, it goes to increase the entropy of the Universe.

5. For those who wish to explore superstring theory, I suggest the following two books, both of which are readable for lay persons.

    Michio Kaku and Jennifer Trainer, *Beyond Einstein: The Cosmic Quest for the Theory of the Universe*, 1987, published by Bantam Books.

    James Trefil, *The Dark Side of the Universe: A Scientist Explores the Mysteries of the Cosmos*, 1988, Charles Scribner's Sons.

Chapter Two

REFERENCES:

The following are general references for this chapter, specifics are noted separately.

Robert Augros & George Stanciu, *The New Biology: Discovering the Wisdom in Nature*, 1988, New Science Library.

Nigel Calder, *Timescale: An Atlas of the Fourth Dimension*, 1983, The Viking Press.

Preston Cloud, *Oasis in Space: Earth History from the Beginning*, 1988, W.W. Norton & Company.

Clair E. Folsome, *The Origin of Life: A Warm Little Pond*, 1979, W.H. Freeman & Company.

Richard Leakey & Roger Lewin, *Origins*, 1977, E.P. Dutton.

_____ , *Origins Reconsidered: In Search of What Makes Us Human*, 1992, Doubleday.

Roger Lewin, *Thread of Life: The Smithsonian Looks at Evolution*, 1982, Distributed by W.W. Norton & Co.

Lynn Margulis & Dorion Sagan, *Micro-cosmos: Four Billion Years of Microbial Evolution*, 1986, Summit Books.

Alexander Marshack, *The Roots of Civilization: The Cognitive Beginnings of Man's First Art, Symbols and Notation*, revised 1991, Moyer Bell Limited.

E.C. Pielou, *After the Ice Age: The Return of Life to Glaciated North America*, 1991, University of Chicago Press.

Frank Press & Raymond Siever, *Earth*, Second Edition, 1978, W.H. Freeman & Co.

Iosif S. Shklovskii, *Stars: Their Birth, Life, and Death*, 1978, W.H. Freeman and Co.

Robert Shapiro, *Origins: A Skeptic's Guide to the Creation of Life on Earth*, 1986, Summit Books.

Steven M. Stanley, *Earth and Life Through Time*, Second Edition, 1989, W.H. Freeman & Co.

_____ , *Extinction*, 1987, Scientific American Library.

———— , *Macroevolution: Pattern and Process*, 1979, W.H. Freeman & Co.

Eric Trinkaus & Pat Shipman, *The Neandertals: Changing the Image of Mankind*, 1992, Alfred A. Knopf.

NOTES:

1. The four known forces are: gravity, electromagneticsm, the strong and weak forces. The latter two operate at the atomic level and are influential in the thermonuclear process.

2. Supernovas are not frequent relative to our concept of time. Not many astronomers have the delight of observing a nearby event. A few were rewarded in February, 1987, when a supernova was detected in the Large Magellanic Cloud, the galaxy nearest the Milky Way. Sadly for some of us, it was only visible to those south of the Equator.

3. Steven W. Stahler, in *Scientific American*, July, 1991, page 48, describes his version of the birth of stars and planetary systems. The article contains excellent graphics to illustrate the text.

4. Previously, external skeletons in the form of shells or cartilage protected and supported body weight in early life forms. The buoyancy provided by water required less internal strength of limbs, spine, etc.

5. I include more detail concerning the emergence of man and human culture in an earlier book, *The Ugly Face of Power: And Masks of Deception*, 1993, University Editions, Inc.

6. Refer to references above.

Chapter Three

NOTES:

1. I don't recall where I read this. If I knew the source I'd gladly give the author credit.

2. Newton's Second Law dealing with dynamics (bodies in motion) reduces to a simple equation F=ma; where F equals force, m equals mass, a equals acceleration. Time enters a twice, meaning that time is squared.

3. For those interested in a lengthy discussion of relativity and a scientific view of time, read: *The Arrow of Time: A Voyage Through Science to Solve Time's Greatest Mystery*, 1990, by Peter Coveney & Roger Highfield, published by Ballantime Books.

4. Published in 1986 by Scientific Books, Inc.

5. The equation describing special relativity is quite short: $E=mc^2$; where e equals energy, m equals mass, and c is the speed of light. This equation states that a little bit of mass will generate bundles of energy, or if transposed, a lot of energy will produce a speck of mass. The equation assumes a process having 100% efficiency (not possible with existing technology). Nuclear fusion is the best we can now do.

6. Nigel Calder, in his 1979 book, *Einstein's Universe*, published by The Viking Press, describes the technique and results of these experiments. This book is recommended as easy reading for anyone interested in the basic concepts of relativity.

Chapter Four

NOTES:

1. Michael E. Long, in the June, 1991, issue of *National Geographic*, gives an excellent overview of recent research covering this topic.

   Kenneth J. Lohmann presents an interesting hypothesis concerning turtle navigation in the January, 1992, issue of *Scientific American*.

   Both articles provide an interesting exposition of the phenomenon, neither give a convincing account of how it is achieved.

2. Francis Hitching, adapted from *The Mysterious World: An Atlas of the Unexplained*, 1978, Holt, Rinehart and Winston.

3. See Note 3, Chapter 3.

4. From Brian O'Leary, Ph.D., *Exploring Inner and Outer Space: A Scientist's Perspective on Personal and Planetary Transformation*, 1989, North Atlantic Books.

5. Rupert Sheldrake, from his book, *The Presence of the Past: Morphic Resonance and the Habits of Nature*, 1988, Vintage Books.

6. Fred Alan Wolf, *Parallel Universes: The Search for Other Worlds*, 1988, Simon and Schuster.

Chapter Five

NOTES:

1. From Stephen W. Hawking's, *A Brief History of Time: From the Big Bang to Black Holes*, 1988, Bantam Books. Thanks to Stephen Hawking and the Permissions Department of Bantam Books for use of this material.

2. John G. Neihardt, *Black Elk Speaks: Being the Life Story of a Holy Man of the Oglala Sioux*, 1932, now available from the University of Nebraska Press.

3. From Joseph Epes Brown's book, *The Spiritual Legacy of the American Indian*, 1982, The Crossroad Publishing Co.

Chapter Six

NOTES:

1. See Note 1, Chapter One.

2. Absolute Unknowable: a term often used by Joseph Campell, renowned authority on mythologies of the world.

3. Dr. Raymond A. Moody, Jr., M.D., *Life After Life*, 1975, Bantam Books.

———— , *Reflections on Life After Life*, 1977, Bantam/Mockingbird Books.
———— , *The Light Beyond*, 1988, Bantam Books.
———— , with Paul Perry, *Coming Back: A Psychiatrist Explores Past-Life Journeys*, 1991, Bantam Books.

4. Still in print and available from E.P. Dutton and Company, Inc. Highly recommended, both for historical content and studies of the paranormal.

Chapter Seven

NOTES:

1. Robert A. Monroe, *Journeys Out of the Body*, 1971, originally published by Doubleday & Co.

2. Carlos Castaneda, *The Teachings of Don Juan*, 1968.
———— , *A Separate Reality*, 1968.
———— , *Journey to Ixtlan*, 1971.
———— , *Tales of Power*, 1974.

3. Dick Sutphen has written numerous books and conducted seminars throughout the United States. I have attended two seminars which featured pastlife regressions. His first two books are most notable:
———— , *You Were Born to Be Together*, 1976.
———— , *Past Lives, Future Loves*, 1978

4. Former astronaut and moon-walker Edgar Mitchell founded the *Institute of Noetic Sciences* in 1973. The Institute funds and initiates scientific research concerning mind and consciousness; it publishes a quarterly review to update members on current work. If interested, write to the Institute at: 475 Gate Five Road, Suite 300, Sausalito, CA 94965.

5. Listed below are just a few books which discuss the origin of life on Earth. Don't expect to find an answer; nothing has been

written which adequately describes origins. These are a cross-section discussing theories and the research which has taken place.

Robert Augros and George Stanciu, see References in Chapter Two.

Clair Edwin Folsome, see References, Chapter Two.

Fred Hoyle and N.C. Wickramasinghe, *Lifecloud: The Origin of Life in the Universe*, 1978, Harper & Row Publishers.

Lynn Margulis and Dorion Sagan, see References in Chapter Two.

Robert Shapiro, Origins: See References in Chapter Two.

Steven M. Stanley, *The New Evolutionary Timetable: Fossils, Genes, and the Origin of Species*, 1981, Basic Books, Inc.

6. Those interested in the history of computer modeling and the emerging science of chaos and complexity are referred to M. Mitchell Waldrop's book, *Complexity: The Emerging Science at the Edge of Order and Chaos*, 1992, Simon & Schuster.

7. Refer to Augros and Stanciu above.

8. Robert Ardrey, *The Territorial Imperative: A Personal Inquiry Into the Animal Origins of Property and Nations*, 1966, now available from Bantam Books.

9. The epic period of paleoanthropology (the study of pre-historic hominids) is well told by three recent books, *Origins Reconsidered, The Neandertals*, and *The Roots of Civilization*, (reference in Chapter Two).

10. Brian L. Weiss, M.D., *Many Lives, Many Masters*, 1988, A Fireside Book (Simon & Schuster).
——— , *Through Time Into Healing*, 1992, Simon & Schuster.

Also Suggested:

Frederick Lenz, Ph.D., *Lifetimes: True Accounts of Reincarnation,* 1979, The Bobbs-Merrill Company, Inc.

Dick Sutphen's two books, referenced above.

11. From an article by David B. Chamberlain, *The Outer Limits of Memory,* in the Autumn, 1990, Noetic Science Review, a publication of the Institute of Noetic Science, Note 4 above.

12. My spelling of cakra and this description of the heart and crown cakras conforms with Joesph Campbell's discussion in *Transformations of Myth Through Time,* 1990, Harper & Row.

13. For those interested in nonlinear dynamical systems, the following two books are recommended. They are written with the lay reader in mind.

    John Briggs and F. David Peat, *Turbulent Mirror: An Illustrated Guide to Chaos Theory and the Science of Wholeness,* 1989, Harper & Row.

    James Gleick, *Chaos: Making a New Science,* 1987, Penguin Books.

14. The implications of nonlinear dynamics on mind and brain are reviewed in the final chapter of *The 3-Pound Universe: Revolutionary Discoveries About the Brain From the Chemistry of the Mind to the New Frontiers of the Soul,* 1986, by Judith Hooper and Dick Teresi, MacMillan Publishing.

15. This sentence is the title of a book, *Order Out of Chaos: Man's New Dialogue With Nature,* 1984, by Nobel Prize winner Ilya Prigogine and Isabelle Stengers, Bantam Books. Somewhat technical, the work is nonetheless an important contribution toward understanding systems which are far from equilibrium.

Chapter Eight

NOTES:

1. From Mircea Eliade, *A History of Religious Ideas: Volume 1*, translated from the French by Willard R. Trask, 1978, The University of Chicago Press.

2. These 12 protons, having like charge, repel each other and without another force the nucleus would explode. Called the strong force, it is extremely strong over a very short distance. The strong force is one of the four known universal forces.

Chapter Nine

NOTES:

1. Wallace Black Elk as told to William S. Lyon, *Black Elk: The Sacred Ways of the Lakota*, 1990, Harper & Row, Publishers, San Francisco.

2. From Gary A. Kowalski, *The Souls of Animals*, 1991, Stillpoint Publishing.

Index

Ordering Information

☐ ***Black Holes & Tepee Rings:*** $13.00 plus $1.50 shipping & handling at book rate. Priority mail—an additional $2.00.

☐ ***The Ugly Face Of Power: And Masks Of Deception,*** *1993:* $10.95 plus $1.50 shipping & handling. Priority mail $2.00 extra.

This is an analysis of aggression, political atrocities, and institutional indulgences/corruption; and the changes necessary to bring about reform.

Two or more of the above books (mixed titles o.k.) shipped postage free via book rate anywhere in the U.S.A.

Please send check or money order (no C.O.D.'s) to:

Black Wolf Productions
P.O. Box 565
Kalispell, Montana 59903

Retail Outlets: For quantity discounts, please check with your distributor/wholesaler, or send for dealer price schedule on letterhead stationery.

Satisfaction Guaranteed: If not totally satisfied, return any book for refund, no questions asked.